General Psychology: A Laboratory Manual

SEVENTH EDITION

Editors:
Barbara Lusk
Aimee Johnson

Contributing Authors:
William Adler
Roberta Benavides
Sally Davis
Martha Ellis
Aimee Johnson
Dan Lipscomb
Barbara Lusk
Jennifer Brooks
Kathy Meyer
Marti Weaver
Debbie White

Collin County Community College

Bent Tree Press
CUSTOM BOOKS

Printed in the United States of America.

ISBN: 1-933005-72-6

Bent Tree Press

59 Damonte Ranch Parkway, #B 284 • Reno, NV 89521 • (800) 970-1883

www.benttreepress.com

Address all correspondence and order information to the above address.

TO THE STUDENT:

Welcome to General psychology. Whether you are planning a career in psychology, teaching, nursing, engineering, business, etc., or taking this course to gain personal insight about yourself and others, we hope you will find this a useful and an exciting course.

This laboratory manual contains a variety of laboratory experiences designed from pertinent research. The exercises provide actual experimentation in conjunction with the topics covered in your textbook. The laboratory component of this course was written in order to provide you with experiences to enhance your understanding of yourself, others, and the field of psychology.

TABLE OF CONTENTS

UNIT 9 – INTELLIGENCE

UNIT 10 – HEALTH PSYCHOLOGY

UNIT 11 – DEVELOPMENTAL

UNIT 12 – PERSONALITY

UNIT 13 – PSYCHOLOGICAL DISORDERS/THERAPY

UNIT 14 – SOCIAL PSYCHOLOGY

REFERENCES

UNIT

1

Introduction

HUMAN NATURE DEBATE

There are five theoretical perspectives which psychologists use to interpret behavior. These perspectives include the (1) psychoanalytic, (2) behavioral, (3) humanistic, (4) cognitive, and (5) neuropsychological perspectives. Among these theories, there are many sharply conflicting views about the essence of human nature. The purpose of this exercise is to conduct a debate in order to further develop understanding of these theoretical perspectives, to advance critical thinking skills, as well as to help students understand their own beliefs about human nature.

Materials: None

Procedure:
1. Your instructor will put a sign in each corner of the classroom indicating "strongly agree," "agree," "disagree," and "strongly disagree." There will be no "neutral" position.

2. Your instructor will then read one of the statements about human nature listed below.

3. You will then get up and move to the corner of the classroom which best represents your level of agreement with the statement.

4. The instructor will then moderate a critical thinking debate on this human nature issue.

5. During the course of the debate, keep these things in mind:

   (a) Give concrete, real life examples to support your view.

   (b) Listen carefully to the argument made by your opponents and try to address each point with a logical counter point.

   (c) DO NOT resort to personal attacks or insults to discredit your opponents' arguments. The debate should be logical and friendly, not personal and emotional.

   (d) Keep in mind that these are philosophical issues. That is, there is no true right or wrong position to take.

HUMAN NATURE DEBATE – CONT.

6.   Your instructor will choose from the following list of statements (or may bring in additional ones).

(a)   Humans are, by nature, selfish and self-centered.

(b)   Once the personality is developed (into adulthood), it cannot be changed. The adult personality is set and continuous.

(c)   People are responsible for their emotions, and therefore can control their emotional reactions to life events.

(d)   All human behaviors are learned. In humans, there are no innate behaviors.

(e)   All human behaviors are ultimately motivated by unconscious drives for sexual pleasure.

THEORETICAL PERSPECTIVES

Psychology has a relatively short history, with researchers first applying the scientific method to questions about human behavior and mental processes as recently as the late 1800's. Several major schools of thought regarding the proper focus of this new science have emerged since the creation of the first formal psychological lab in 1879. You are to review both the historical foundation of psychology and the more recent major perspectives in the field.

Materials: Text and related readings (use LRC holdings and Internet)

Procedure: Students will divide into small groups, with each group choosing one theoretical perspective to research. Group members will divide the workload so that each member has a portion of the report to write. Members then consolidate each portion into a summary that is presented to the class.

The summary should include, but is not limited to, information regarding historical context, key concepts, main contributors, and goals of therapy.

Perspectives include the following: Structuralism, Functionalism, Psychodynamic, Behaviorism, Gestalt, Humanism, Cognitive, Evolutionary, and Neuropsychology.

U N I T

2 Research Methods

ANALYSIS OF A JOURNAL ARTICLE

You are to choose a journal article related to psychology. Current journals are available in the college library.

Materials: Current journal article.

Procedure: Read the article and write a paper answering the following questions:

1.   Summarize the information contained in the article.

2.   Evaluate the information in the discussion.
    Did the author's conclusions follow logically from the results reported?
    Were there alternative explanations offered for the results?
    What were they?
    What future research can be suggested?

3.   What is your opinion of the article?

EXPERIMENTAL DESIGN

Research is the backbone of psychology. In this exercise you will learn the technique of posing research questions and designing the studies to answer these questions.

Materials: Laboratory report forms

Procedure: You will design a research study that meets the criteria of experimental research. Each member of the class will be randomly assigned to a small group. Once you are in your designated groups, you will decide on a topic that will lend itself to experimental research.   You will then construct the design using the questions/statements on your laboratory report form as your outline. YOU DO NOT CONDUCT THE EXPERIMENT!

LABORATORY REPORT FORM: EXPERIMENTAL DESIGN

You are ready to start your study. Remember details are important!

1.   Our hypothesis is:

2.   Our independent variable:

3.   Our dependent variable:

4.   Define the key elements in the study (e.g. The number of subjects who will participate, the setting, the specific characteristics of the variable of interest, etc.)

EXPERIMENTAL DESIGN - CONT.

5.   What is the operational definition of the behavior to be studied?

6.   Are you using a pre-test and post-test? If so, describe.

7.   What is your treatment or how are you manipulating your variables? Include the controls you are using.

UNIT

3

Physiology

LEARNING STYLES TEST

The left and right hemispheres of the cerebral cortex have some functional differences. These differences are often expressed in the way people live their daily lives. One of many expressions of left or right hemisphere dominance is seen in how a person learns in both formal and informal learning environments.

Materials: Torrance Learning Styles Inventory

Procedure: For this exercise, you will be taking the Torrance Learning Styles Inventory (TLSI). The TLSI is a diagnostic test used for two primary purposes. First, the results are used by teachers to understand the learning style make-up of a class in order to teach in a style most suitable for that class. Second, the results are useful for individual students to become more aware of their style of learning so they can study in a manner best suited to their learning style.

Your instructor will administer the TLSI to you. Mark your answers on the following answer form, and interpret your results. Answer the summary questions on your laboratory report form.

TORRANCE ANSWER SHEET

CHOOSE ONLY ONE ANSWER FOR EACH QUESTION. Circle the appropriate letter for each question.

1. A B C	11. A B C	21. A B C	31. A B C	41. A B C
2. A B C	12. A B C	22. A B C	32. A B C	42. A B C
3. A B C	13. A B C	23. A B C	33. A B C	43. A B C
4. A B C	14. A B C	24. A B C	34. A B C	44. A B C
5. A B C	15. A B C	25. A B C	35. A B C	45. A B C
6. A B C	16. A B C	26. A B C	36. A B C	46. A B C
7. A B C	17. A B C	27. A B C	37. A B C	47. A B C
8. A B C	18. A B C	28. A B C	38. A B C	48. A B C
9. A B C	19. A B C	29. A B C	39. A B C	49. A B C
10. A B C	20. A B C	30. A B C	40. A B C	50. A B C

SCORING:

1.   Compute total number of A's _____,

         total number of B's _____,

         total number of C's _____.

2.   Compute total number of B's minus total number of A's. It can be a positive or negative number.____

3.   If your number of C's is 15 or higher, you must now divide your B minus A score by three._____

      OR If you number of C's is between 9 and 14, you must divide your B minus A score by two._____

      OR If your number of C's is 8 or less, do not divide at all. In this case, your B minus A score is your final score._____

4.   Plot your score below.

-14 –13 –12 –11 –10 –9 –8 –7 –6 –5 –4 –3 –2 -1 0 +1 +2 +3 +4 +5 +6 +7 +8 +9 +10 +11 +12 +13 +14

-2,-1=Slightly Left Dominant   +2,+3=Slightly Right Dominant

-4,-5,-6=Moderate Left Dominant   +4,+5,+6=Moderate Right Dominant

-7,through-14=Strong Left Dominant   +7,through+14=Strong Right Dominant

                              -1,0,1=Co-Dominant

YOUR STYLE OF LEARNING AND THINKING

Left Mode . . . . .Right Mode

* Rational	* Intuitive
* Responds to verbal instructions and explanations	* Responds to demonstrated, illustrated or symbolic instructions
* Experiments systematically and with control; prefers solving problems by breaking them down into parts, then approaching the problem sequentially, using logic.	* Experiments randomly with less restraint; prefers solving problems by looking at the whole, the configurations, then approaching the problem through patterns, using hunches.
* Makes objective judgments, extrinsic to the person.	* Makes subjective judgments, intrinsic to person.
* Planned and structured.	* Fluid and spontaneous.
* Prefers factual information.	* Prefers abstract information.
* Analytic reader.	* Synthesizing reader.
* Primary reliance on language in thinking and remembering.	* Primary reliance on images in thinking and remembering.
* Prefers talking and writing.	* Prefers drawing and manipulating objects.
* Prefers multiple choice tests.	* Prefers open-ended questions.
* Prefers work/study carefully planned.	* Prefers work/study open/ended.
* Prefers hierarchical authority structures.	* Prefers participative authority structures.
* Controls feelings.	* More free with feelings.
* Responds best to auditory, visual stimuli.	* Responds best to kinetic stimuli (movement, action)
* Responsive to structure of environment.	* Essentially self-acting.
* Rarely uses metaphors and analogies.	* Frequently uses metaphors and analogies.

LEARNING STYLES TEST – CONT.

Summary Questions:

1.   What learning style do you have? (Specify left, right, co-dominant, slight, moderate, strong.)

2.   List the characteristics of your learning style that you believe fit you well. (Co-dominants, choose from all characteristics.)

3.   List any characteristics of your learning style you believe do not fit you well.

4.   Write a brief essay relating your learning style type to how you actually learn in both formal (classroom) and informal (daily life) settings. Use specific examples from your past experience to illustrate how the characteristics of your learning style do or do not fit your actual style of learning.

UNIT

4

Sensation & Perception

SMELL AND TASTE INTERACTION

This activity illustrates how cues can combine in complex ways to produce sensory experiences usually taken for granted, such as taste.

Materials: Containers, food samples and blindfolds.

Procedure: To show how food preference results from a combination of taste and smell, four identical containers will have bite size cubes of each of the foods your instructor has chosen. Three "taste study" volunteers will leave the room. The rest of the class will be informed by the instructor as to which container has which food item. Next, the volunteers will enter into the room, one at a time, blindfolded with their nostrils closed off. The chunks of food will be fed to the subject in random order. The instructor will then ask the subject what is being tasted.

Record the subjects' responses on the table for recording answers provided on the following page.

Answer summary questions on the laboratory report form.

TABLE FOR RECORDING ANSWERS

Trial #_____

Sample Given

Subject's guess

Trial #_____

Sample Given

Subject's guess

Trial #_____

Sample Given

Subject's guess

SMELL AND TASTE INTERACTION – CONT.

Summary Questions:

1.   Were you surprised by the "taste study" volunteers' responses? If so, why?

2.   Describe how your own food preferences are affected by olfactory and taste cues.

3.   What happens to taste when you have a head cold? Why?

PERCEPTUAL ILLUSIONS AND PRINCIPLES

This activity provides opportunities for identifying perceptual illusions and commenting on the principals involved in these illusions.

Materials: None

Procedure: Look at each example of perceptual illusions and answer the summary questions that follow each illusion.

1. The Paggendorf Illusion

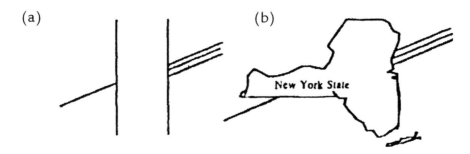

(a)   (b)

For each figure, indicate which line represents the continuation of the diagonal line on the left. Now, use a straight edge to determine whether or not you were correct. Were you surprised by the results? Why or why not?

2. The Gestalt Law of Pragnanz:

Look at the figures shown for just a moment, turn the page over, and reproduce them on another sheet. Now, compare your drawings with the originals. Do you see any differences? If so, what are they?

PERCEPTUAL ILLUSIONS AND PRINCIPLES – CONT.

3.   Context Effects:

A, B, C, D, E, F
10, 11, 12, 13, 14

My phone number is area code

604,876-1569, Please call!

Look at the series of letters and numbers. Do you notice anything unusual? If so, indicate what you noticed.

4. The Oblique Effect:

Stand back from the three stimuli shown until you can no longer clearly see the oblique lines in the center circle. The design should appear uniformly gray. What happens to the lines in the left and right circles?

UNIT

5

Motivation and Emotion

ARE YOU A HIGHLY SENSITIVE PERSON?

Are you a highly sensitive person? According to research psychologist Elaine Aron (1996) highly sensitive people (HSP) have sensitive nervous systems; therefore, they are easily overaroused. They are often overstimulated by stimuli that most people can easily tune out (noise, lights, smells, etc.). This lower threshold for arousal can lead to feelings of being overwhelmed, or being overstressed because the arousal is mislabeled as fear or anxiety.

On the other hand, HSP's are more aware of subtleties in their environment, noticing things that others may overlook. This contributes to a stronger sense of intuition, conscientiousness and insightful creativity. They also tend to process information at deeper levels of semantic memory, often thinking about their own thinking. The trait of being highly sensitive is viewed as neutral, although it can be perceived as negative if misunderstood or undervalued, or as positive, if the remarkable abilities are emphasized and valued. The following is not a diagnostic tool, but a questionnaire designed to enhance self-knowledge and understanding.

Materials: Are You a Highly Sensitive Person questionnaire

Procedure: Respond to the questionnaire. Answer each question according to the way you personally feel. Answer true if it is at least somewhat true for you; false if it is not very true or not at all true for you.

Answer the summary questions on your laboratory report form.

ARE YOU HIGHLY SENSITIVE?

T F 1.   I am easily overwhelmed by strong sensory input.

T F 2.   I seem to be aware of subtleties in my environment.

T F 3.   Other people's moods affect me.

T F 4.   I tend to be very sensitive to pain.

T F 5.   I find myself needing to withdraw during busy days, into bed or into a darkened room or any place where I can have some privacy and relief from stimulation.

T F 6.   I am particularly sensitive to the effects of caffeine.

T F 7.   I am easily overwhelmed by things like bright lights, strong smells, coarse fabrics, or sirens close by.

T F 8.   I have a rich, complex inner life.

T F 9.   I am made uncomfortable by loud noises.

T F 10.   I am deeply moved by the arts or music.

T F 11.   My nervous system sometimes feels so frazzled that I just have to get off by myself.

T F 12.   I am conscientious.

T F 13.   I startle easily.

T F 14.   I get rattled when I have a lot to do in a short amount of time.

T F 15.   When people are uncomfortable in a physical environment I tend to know what needs to be done to make it more comfortable (like changing the lighting or the seating).

ARE YOU HIGHLY SENSITIVE? – CONT.

T F 16.   I am annoyed when people try to get me to do too many things at once.

T F 17.   I try hard to avoid making mistakes or forgetting things.

T F 18.   I make a point to avoid violent movies and TV shows.

T F 19.   I become unpleasantly aroused when a lot is going on around me.

T F 20.   Being very hungry creates a strong reaction in me, disrupting my concentration or mood.

T F 21.   Changes in my life shake me up.

T F 22.   I notice and enjoy delicate or fine scents, tastes, sounds, works of art.

T F 23.   I find it unpleasant to have a lot going on at once.

T F 24.   I make it a high priority to arrange my life to avoid upsetting or overwhelming situations.

T F 25.   I am bothered by intense stimuli, like loud noises or chaotic scenes.

T F 26.   When I must compete or be observed while performing a task, I become so nervous or shaky that I do much worse than I would otherwise.

T F 27.   When I was a child, my parents or teachers seemed to see me as sensitive or shy.

SCORING THE SELF-TEST FOR HIGH SENSITIVITY

If you answered more than fourteen of the questions as true of yourself, you are probably highly sensitive.

No psychological test is so accurate that an individual should base his or her life on the results. Psychologists try to develop good questions and then decide on the cut-off based on the average response. If fewer questions are true of you, but extremely true, that might also justify calling you highly sensitive.

Laboratory Report Form-

Summary Questions:

Answer the following questions completely and thoughtfully.

1.   Based on your questionnaire results, do you think you are highly sensitive? (Remember, if only a few are extremely true, you may be highly sensitive)

2.   Although Aron sees HSP's as having a neutral trait, she recognizes that all cultures make value judgements on personality traits. Do you think our culture judges the HSP in a negative, positive or neutral manner? What evidence do you see for your answer? (e.g. media figures, popular personalities, experiences, etc.)

3.   Do you personally view being highly sensitive as positive, negative or neutral? Why? Name some advantages and disadvantages of having this trait.

UNMASKING THE FACE

Eckman and Friesen explain how different facial expressions reflect the emotions of surprise, fear, disgust, anger, happiness, and sadness. This exercise was designed to help you become a more adept observer of facial expressions.

Materials: Laboratory Manual pages.

Procedure: On the following page(s) there are eighteen faces revealing either a basic emotion or a mixture of emotions. Write down in the space provided under each of the faces which emotion(s) you feel is being represented.

UNMASKING THE FACE – CONT.

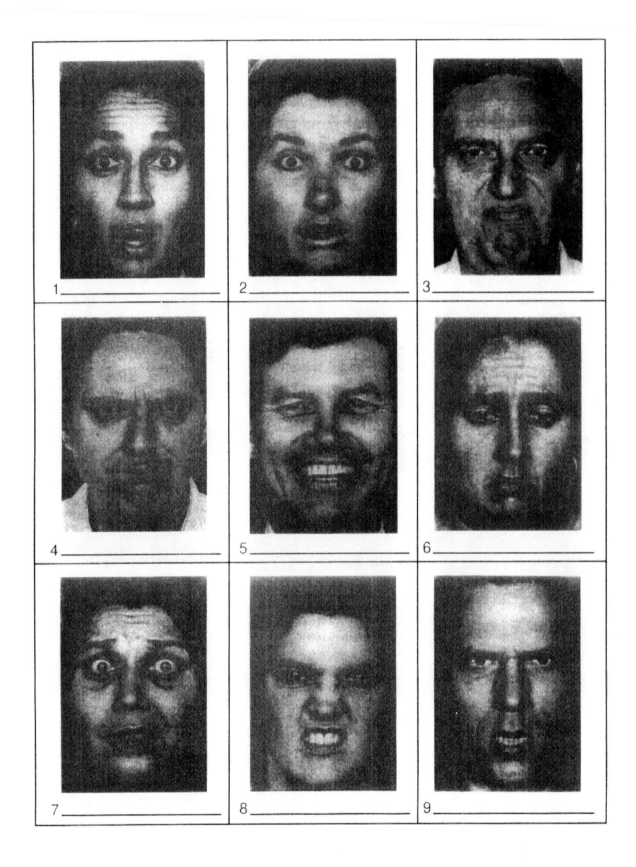

UNMASKING THE FACE – CONT.

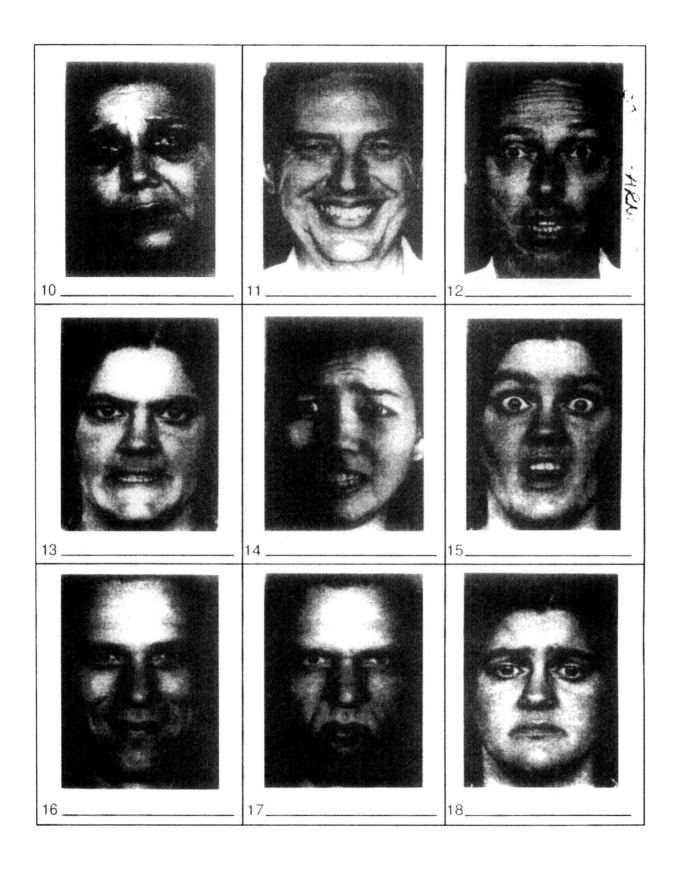

UNMASKING THE FACE – CONT.

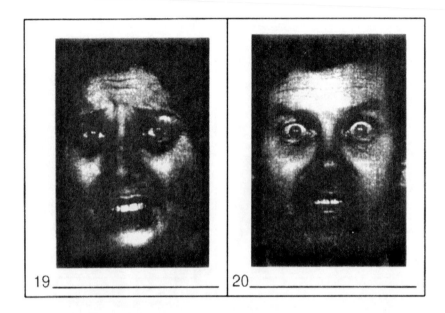

19 _____   20 _____

Laboratory Report Form-
Summary Questions:

1.   Which emotions were easiest to judge?

2.   What rules did you use in order to read the faces?

3.   What are cultural display rules and how do they affect facial expression?

IDENTIFYING HUMAN NEEDS

Maslow's model of motivation considers different motivational needs to be ordered in a hierarchy; basic needs must be met first, followed by the higher order needs.

Maslow's Hierarchy of Needs:

5.   Self-Actualization Needs
4.   Esteem Needs
3.   Belonging Needs
2.   Safety Needs
1.   Physiological Needs

Materials: Laboratory Report Form

Procedure: Divide into groups and read each of the statements below. Write in the space provided the need that you feel is most likely the dominant need felt by the person speaking. The list of needs that you can choose from are shown above.

_____ 1.   "Have I got a terrible headache. It's really splitting."

_____ 2.   "It gets lonely in my apartment on the weekends. My roommate goes to visit her parents and most of my neighbors are away, too."

_____ 3.   "I feel really bored by this course. It's a lot like the one I took last year. I was hoping it would be more challenging."

_____ 4.   "He really makes me furious. I'm tired of his put-downs! Who does he think he is anyway?"

_____ 5.   "Uh, listen, do you mind if we don't go into that nightclub? I hear that some tough types hang out there and that someone got beaten up there last week."

_____ 6.   "Hey, guess what? I just got an A on my term paper. Pretty good, eh?"

_____ 7.   "I've decided to leave home and get an apartment of my own. My parents are upset, but I just want to make it on my own."

SENSATION-SEEKING SCALE

People differ in their tendency to seek out stimulation and novelty. Marvin Zuckerman (1979) developed a psychological test to measure the sensation seeking motive and its effects on behavior.

Materials: Sensation Seeking Scale

Procedure: For each item circle the choice (A or B) that best describes how you feel or what you like. Please make only one choice for each item. If the decision is difficult, choose the one that best describes your likes or feelings. If you do not like either choice, circle the choice you dislike least. There are no right or wrong answers. Be honest in your appraisal of yourself.

1. A.   I would like a job that requires a lot of traveling.
    B.   I would prefer a job in one location.

2. A.   I am invigorated by a brisk, cold day.
    B.   I can't wait to get indoors on a cold day.

3. A.   I find a certain pleasure in routine kinds of work.
    B.   Although they are sometimes necessary, I usually dislike routine kinds of work.

4. A.   I often wish I could be a mountain climber.
    B.   I can't understand people who risk their necks climbing mountains.

5. A.   I dislike all body odors.
    B.   I like some of the earthy body smells.

6. A.   I get bored seeing the same old faces.
    B.   I like the comfortable familiarity of everyday friends.

7. A.   I like to explore a strange city or section of town by myself, even if it means getting lost.
    B.   I prefer a guide when I am in a place I don't know well.

8. A.   I find the quickest and easiest route to a place and stick to it.
    B.   I sometimes take different routes to a place I often go to, just for variety's sake.

SENSATION-SEEKING SCALE – CONT.

9. A. I would not like to try any drug that might produce strange or dangerous effects on me.
    B. I would like to try some of the drugs that produce hallucinations.

10. A. I would prefer living in an ideal society where everyone is safe, secure, and happy.
    B. I would have preferred living in the unsettled days of our past.

11. A. I sometimes like to do things that are a little frightening.
    B. A sensible person avoids activities that are dangerous.

12. A. I order dishes with which I am familiar, so as to avoid disappointment and unpleasantness.
    B. I like to try new foods that I have never tasted before.

13. A. I can't stand riding with a person who likes to speed.
    B. I sometimes like to drive very fast because I find it exciting.

14. A. If I were a salesperson, I would prefer a straight salary rather than the risk of making little or nothing on a commission basis.
    B. If I were a sales person, I would prefer working on commission, if I had a chance to make more money than I could make on a salary.

15. A. I would like to take up the sport of water-skiing.
    B. I would not like to take up the sport of water-skiing.

16. A. I don't like to argue with people whose beliefs are sharply divergent from mine, because such arguments are never resolved.
    B. I find people who disagree with my beliefs more stimulating than people who agree with me.

SENSATION-SEEKING SCALE – CONT.

17. A. When I go on a trip, I like to plan my route and timetable fairly carefully.
    B. I would like to take off on a trip with no preplanned or definite routes or timetables.

18. A. I enjoy the thrills of watching car races.
    B. I find car races unpleasant.

19. A. Most people spend entirely too much money on life insurance.
    B. Life insurance is something that no one can afford to be without.

20. A. I would like to learn to fly an airplane.
    B. I would not like to learn to fly an airplane.

21. A. I would not like to be hypnotized.
    B. I would like to have the experience of being hypnotized.

22. A. The most important goal of life is to live it to the fullest and experience as much of it as you can.
    B. The most important goal of life is to find peace and happiness.

23. A. I would like to try parachute jumping.
    B. I would never want to try jumping out of a plane, with or without a parachute.

24. A. I enter cold water gradually, giving myself time to get used to it.
    B. I like to dive or jump right into the ocean or a cold pool.

25. A. I do not like the irregularity and discord of most modern music.
    B. I like to listen to new and unusual kinds of music.

26. A. I prefer friends who are excitingly unpredictable.
    B. I prefer friends who are reliable and predictable.

27. A. When I go on a vacation, I prefer the comfort of a good room and bed.
    B. When I go on a vacation, I prefer the change of camping out.

SENSATION-SEEKING SCALE – CONT.

28. A. The essence of good art is in its clarity, symmetry of form, and harmony of colors.
     B. I often find beauty in the clashing colors and irregular forms of modern paintings.

29. A. The worst social sin is to be rude.
     B. The worst social sin is to be a bore.

30. A. I look forward to a good night of rest after a long day.
     B. I wish I didn't have to waste so much of a day sleeping.

31. A. I prefer people who are emotionally expressive even if they are a bit unstable.
     B. I prefer people who are calm and even-tempered.

32. A. A good painting should shock or jolt the senses.
     B. A good painting should give one a feeling of peace and security.

33. A. When I feel discouraged, I recover by relaxing and having some soothing diversion.
     B. When I feel discouraged, I recover by going out and doing something new and exciting.

34. A. People who ride motorcycles must have some kind of an unconscious need to hurt themselves.
     B. I would like to drive or ride on a motorcycle.

SENSATION-SEEKING SCALE SCORING

The scoring key is reproduced below. Circle your response of A or B each time it corresponds to the keyed response below. Add up the number of responses you circled; this total is your score on the Sensation-Seeking Scale. Record your score below.

1. A	8. B	15. A	22. A	29. B
2. A	9. B	16. B	23. A	30. B
3. B	10. B	17. B	24. B	31. A
4. A	11. A	18. A	25. B	32. A
5. B	12. B	19. A	26. A	33. B
6. A	13. B	20. A	27. B	34. B
7. A	14. B	21. B	28. B	

MY SCORE_____

WHAT THE SCALE MEASURES

As its name implies, the Sensation-Seeking Scale (SSS) measures one's need for a high level of stimulation. As discussed in your text, sensation-seeking involves the active pursuit of experience which many people would find very stressful. Marvin Zuckerman (1979) believes that this thirst for sensation is a general personality trait that leads people to seek thrills, adventures and new experiences.

RESEARCH ON THE SCALE

The scale which you just responded to is the second version of the SSS. Test-retest reliabilities are quite respectable and there is minimal contamination by social desirability bias. There is ample evidence to support the scale's validity. For example, studies show that high sensation-seekers appraise hypothetical situations as less risky than low sensation-seekers and are more willing to volunteer for an experiment in which they will by hypnotized. The scale also shows robust positive correlations with measures of change-seeking, novelty-seeking, extraversion and impulsiveness. Interestingly, SSS scores tend to decline with increasing age.

INTERPRETING YOUR SCORE

Our norms are based on percentiles reported by Zuckerman and colleagues for a sample of 62 undergraduates. Although males generally tend to score a bit higher than females on the SSS, the differences are small enough to report one set of (averaged) norms. Remember, sensation-seeking scores tend to decline with age. So, if you're not in the modal college student age range (17-23) these norms may be a bit high.

SENSATION-SEEKING SCALE SCORING – CONT.

High Score:	20-34	(roughly more than 1 standard deviation about the mean)
Intermediate Score:	11-20	(within 1 standard deviation of the mean either way)
Low Score:	0-10	(roughly more than 1 standard deviation below the mean)

High Scorers: You thrive on sensation. You probably are easily bored and need to be challenged. People such as yourself satisfy their need for stimulation by seeking adventures, taking risks, pursuing unusual experiences (such as hypnosis or meditation), partying, gambling, traveling frequently, experimenting with drugs and so forth. While you may not be drawn to all of the above activities, you nonetheless are quite likely to be bored by routine; you have a thirst for new and different activities, whatever they may be.

Intermediate Scorers: A score in this range suggests that you are roughly average in sensation-seeking. Although you probably do not go out of your way to avoid high stimulation, you probably don't pursue it obsessively either.

Low Scorers: A low score means that you generally find high levels of stimulation to be aversive. The experiences that high sensation-seekers crave do not appeal to you. In fact, you may find them threatening and you may be mystified by others' flirtation with danger. You probably feel comfortable with routine and value security highly. Thrill seeking just isn't your cup of tea.

ADVERTISING AND MOTIVATION

Do advertisers base their campaigns on motivational principles? In this activity you will be evaluating advertisements to find various principles of motivation.

Materials: Magazine advertisements

Procedure: 1.   You are to collect 2 magazine advertisements and bring them to class.

2.   In small groups you will analyze the ads for motivational themes discussed in class and in the textbook. Be sure to relate all or any combination of motivational principles which apply to the ads you have chosen. Answer summary questions on your laboratory report form.

Levels of Maslow's Hierarchy of Needs

* **Self-actualizing Needs-** ad implies using the product will move you to your highest level of functioning. Rarely used.
* **Esteem needs-** ad suggests product will help you like yourself more and others will like you more as well.
* **Love/Belongingness Needs-** ad implies product will help you feel a social and emotional bond with others.
* **Safety Needs-** ad implies product will help you feel more safe and secure.
* **Biological Needs-** ad implies product will help you satisfy your most basic need for food, liquid, and sex.

Social Motives

* **Affiliation Motivation-** ad implies using product will help you feel more a part of a social group, more socially grounded.
* **Achievement Motivation-** ad implies product will help you feel a sense of accomplishment, like you can reach your highest goals. Both you and others will see you as more successful.
* **Power Motivation-** ad implies product will help you gain control over forces in your life.

Psychological Motives

* **Motivation for Novel Stimulation-** ad implies using the product will make your life more interesting (or less boring).
* **Stimulus Seeking Motives-** ad implies using the product will bring extreme excitement to your life. You will brush with danger but somehow escape.

Psychoanalytic Motivational Factors

* **Sexual Motives-** ad attempts to stimulate either conscious, or deep unconscious sexual motives.
* **Death Motives-** ad attempts to stimulate a deep unconscious fixation and preoccupation with the peaceful sleep of death

LABORATORY REPORT FORM: ADVERTISEMENT AND MOTIVATION

Summary Questions:

Magazine Advertisement

1.   Describe the ad visually:

2.   What key words and phrases are used?

3.   For sex-marketed products, which ones are the most blatant and which ones are more subtle?

4.   Are you surprised to find that products are marketed at different levels of motivation? Why or why not?

5.   Explain the motivational principles used to motivate the consumer to purchase the product or service being marketed.

U N I T

6

Consciousness

DREAMS

Sleep takes up approximately 1/3 of our lives. During this 1/3, part of each night is spent in a state called dreaming. Through this assignment you will become more aware of your dreams and their underlying content.

Materials: Pencil and paper beside your bed.

Procedure: 1. Keep a diary of your dreams for one week. Put a pencil and paper beside your bed so that you can record information anytime you wake up. Prior to going to sleep tell yourself to expect to remember your dreams. Close your eyes and visualize yourself dreaming. As you are getting close to falling asleep, repeat over and over to yourself, "When I wake up I will remember my dreams."

Write down as much information as you can remember. Include characters, action involved, time of day, time of year, colors, smells, sounds, emotions, etc. On your laboratory report form write a brief synopsis of each dream.

2. Next you are to analyze each of your dreams by completing the chart on your laboratory report form. Do this for each dream.

Answer the summary questions on the laboratory report form.

LABORATORY REPORT FORM: DREAMS

BRIEF SYNOPSIS OF EACH DREAM (MINIMUM OF 3)

SYNOPSIS (DREAM #1)

SYNOPSIS (DREAM #2)

SYNOPSIS (DREAM #3)

DREAMS – CONT.

ANALYSIS

Analyze each dream by responding to these statements.

Dream #1

Current experiences that led to this dream: _____

Theme(s) expressed in this dream: _____

Symbols (if any): _____

Past experiences (if any): _____

_____

Resolution (if any): _____

_____

Dream #2

Current experiences that led to this dream: _____

Theme(s) expressed in this dream: _____

Symbols (if any): _____

Past experiences (if any): _____

_____

Resolution (if any): _____

_____

Do this for each dream on additional paper.

DREAMS – CONT.

Summary Questions:

1.   Do you see any consistent theme throughout your dreams?

2.   How did analyzing your dreams help you to gain insight about yourself as well as your dreams?

3.   How difficult was it to keep a diary of dreams? Did keeping a diary make you more aware of your dreams?

UNIT

7

Learning

CLASSICAL CONDITIONING

Classical conditioning is a kind of learning in which a previously neutral stimulus comes to elicit a response through its association with a stimulus that naturally brings about the response.

The following lab is taken from a text written by Holland and Skinner, two learning theorists.

Materials: Classical Conditioning questionnaire.

Procedure: 1. The Instructor will assign each student to a small group.

2. Each group will work together to arrive at the answers for each question on the laboratory report form.

3. Each group member will turn in a completed laboratory report form.

4. Remember to work from #1-#29. DO NOT SKIP AHEAD.

5. Refer to the description of Pavlov's experiment on page 68 in order to answer questions. The questions make reference to different elements of the experiment, indicated by letters within parentheses.

CLASSICAL CONDITIONING

(A)   The conditioned reflex was discovered by Pavlov, a Russian physiologist.

(B)   A dog is placed in a special room, free of extraneous stimuli.

(C)   Under anesthesia, a small opening has been made in the dog's cheek and the duct of a salivary gland is brought to the surface where it remains after healing. A tube fastened to the cheek leads to the next room where the experimenter can count the drops of saliva secreted.

(D)   In a typical experiment, a tone is sounded several times. After an early slight disturbance has passed, the dog does not salivate in response to the tone. The tone is called a neutral stimulus because it is ineffective in eliciting salivation.

(E)   When food powder is dropped nearby, the dog eats the powder and salivation occurs. Food powder in the dog's mouth is an unconditioned stimulus, and the salivation it elicits an unconditioned response.

(F)   The sequence of food-in-mouth and salivation is called an unconditioned reflex.

(G)   Next, a new stimulus, a tone (neutral stimulus), is presented either simultaneously with the food (unconditioned stimulus) or just before the food.

(H)   The two stimuli are presented together, or paired, this way many times.

(I)   When the tone is then presented alone, it elicits salivation.

(J)   Conditioning is said to have taken place. The tone is no longer a neutral stimulus; it is a conditioned stimulus.

(K)   In this conditioned reflex, salivation is the conditioned response, and the tone the conditioned stimulus.

(L)   If the tone is now repeatedly presented but no longer paired with food, it loses its power to elicit salivation. The conditioned reflex is said to have been extinguished. This process is called extinction.

THE LETTERS IN PARENTHESES IN THE ACCOMPANYING SET REFER TO THE LETTERS ABOVE.

CLASSICAL CONDITIONING

1. The room in (B) is designed to _____ uncontrolled factors which might affect the experimental result.

2. (C) is used to obtain a measurement of the _____ of the response.

3. In (D), "neutral stimulus" means a tone which ___ ___ effect on salivation before conditioning.

4. Since the tone has no effect on salivation before conditioning, it is a(n) _____ _____ .

5. In (E), the food powder is an unconditioned stimulus in the sense that conditioning _____ necessary to make it an eliciting stimulus.

6. In (E), salivation elicited by food powder is an unconditioned response because food powder elicits salivation even though no _____ has taken place.

7. In (F), the unconditioned reflex has (1) _____ components; an unconditioned (2) _____ and an unconditioned (3) _____ .

8. When a response is elicited by a stimulus without previous conditioning, the sequence is called a(n) _____ _____.

9. According to (G), conditioning will occur only if the two stimuli occur _____ in time.

10. If, instead of the procedure described in (G), the tone had followed the food, the conditions required for _____ would not have been present.

11. As described in (G), the procedure for conditioning a reflex is to pair an initially (1) _____ stimulus with a(n) (2) _____ _____ repeatedly.

12. In (G), little or no conditioning would have occurred if the tone had preceded the food by more than a few seconds. The interval between the stimulus-to-be-conditioned and the unconditioned stimulus must be rather _____.

13. An important aspect of the conditioning procedure is the _____ between presentation of the initially neutral stimulus and of the unconditioned stimulus.

14. The presence of a conditioned reflex is occasionally tested as in (I). It is essential that the unconditioned stimulus, food, ___ ___ presented on these test trials.

CLASSICAL CONDITIONING – CONT.

15. In (J), conditioning is said to have taken place because a previously neutral stimulus is now capable of _____ salivation.

16. A previously neutral stimulus acquires the power to elicit a response in the process called _____.

17. In (K), the tone is called a conditioned stimulus because it elicits the response only after some _____ has taken place.

18. Before conditioning, the tone was a(n) (1)_____ stimulus; after conditioning, the tone has become a(n) (2) _____ stimulus.

19. A tone elicits salivation as a(n) _____ response.

20. The conditioned response, _____, is elicited by the conditioned stimulus, a ____.

21. In (L), the conditioned stimulus is frequently presented _____ the unconditioned stimulus.

22. In (L), the conditioned reflex has been extinguished in the sense that the stimulus has frequently been presented without being _____ with the unconditioned stimulus and has, therefore, lost its ability to elicit the response.

23. In the extinction process, the _____ _____ is presented alone.

24. A new neutral stimulus is able to elicit a response after (1) _____ has taken place. It ceases to do so after (2) _____ has taken place.

25. In Pavlov's famous experiments on conditioning, _____ was the unconditioned response.

26. The process of conditioning was discovered by _____.

27. A stimulus able to elicit a response without previous conditioning is called a(n) (1) _____ _____; a stimulus able to elicit a response only after conditioning is called a(n) (2) _____ _____.

28. A response elicited by a conditioned stimulus is a(n) (1) _____ _____; a response elicited by an unconditioned stimulus is a(n) (2) _____ _____.

29. To condition a reflex, a neutral stimulus is (1) _____ with a(n) (2) _____ _____.

INSTRUMENTAL/OPERANT CONDITIONING

Operant or instrumental conditioning is a type of learning in which the organism acts deliberately in order to produce a particular outcome.

The following lab is taken from a text written by Holland and Skinner, two learning theorists.

Materials: Operant Conditioning questionnaire.

Procedure:
1. The Instructor will assign each student to a small group.

2. Each group will work together to arrive at an answer for each question on the laboratory report form.

3. Each group member will turn in a completed laboratory report form.

4. Remember to work from #1-#30. DO NOT SKIP AHEAD.

LABORTORY REPORT FORM:
INSTRUMENTAL/OPERANT CONDITIONING

Complete the following statements.

1. Performing animals are sometimes trained with "rewards". The behavior of a hungry animal can be "rewarded" with _____.

2. A technical term for "reward" is reinforcement. To "reward" an organism with food is to _____ it with food.

3. Technically speaking, a thirsty organism can be _____ with water.

4. The trainer reinforces the animal by giving it food _____ it has performed correctly.

5. Reinforcement and behavior occur in the temporal order: (1)_____, (2)_____.

6. Food given to a hungry animal does not reinforce a particular response unless it is given almost immediately _____ the response.

7. Unlike a stimulus in a reflex, a reinforcing stimulus _____ _____ act to elicit the response it reinforces.

8. A reinforcement does not elicit a response; it simply makes it more _____ that an animal will respond in the same way again.

9. Food is probably not reinforcing if the animal is not _____.

10. If an animal's response is not followed by reinforcement, similar responses will occur_____ frequently in the future.

11. To make sure an animal will perform, the trainer provides _____ for the response frequently.

12. A hungry pigeon in the park flicks dead leaves about with quick movements of its beak. This behavior is _____ whenever it uncovers bits of food.

13. A pigeon is occasionally reinforced for flicking leaves about because of the common natural arrangement of leaves over _____ .

INSTRUMENTAL/OPERANT CONDITIONING – CONT.

14. The reinforcement used by animal trainers is deliberately arranged, while the arrangement of leaves and food in the park is _____.

15. Food is not reinforcing unless the animal has first been _____ food for some time.

16. Reinforcing a response produces an increase in the _____ that the response will occur again.

17. We do not observe "probability" directly. We say that a response has become more probable if it is observed to occur more _____ under controlled conditions.

18. When a response has been reinforced, it will be emitted _____ frequently in the future.

19. To get an animal to emit a response more frequently, we _____ the response.

20. In laboratory research, various devices are used to reinforce responses. Heat can be used to _____ the responses of a cold animal.

21. An electrically operated food magazine which presents food can be used to reinforce a(n)_____ of an organism deprived of food.

22. If the cold (or food deprived organism turns on an electrically operated heat lamp (or food magazine), the response of turning on will be _____.

23. The response of turning on the electrically operated heat lamp or food magazine will be emitted more _____ in the future if the organism is cold or hungry.

24. In a typical apparatus, the depression of a horizontal bar automatically operates a food magazine. The apparatus selects "bar pressing" as the _____ to be reinforced.

25. The response of pressing a bar must be emitted at least once in order to be _____.

INSTRUMENTAL/OPERANT CONDITIONING – CONT.

26. Since no eliciting stimuli are observed for such responses as flicking leaves or bar pressing, we cannot say that these responses are _____ by stimuli, as are the responses in reflexes.

27. Responses such as bar pressing, flicking leaves, etc., are said to be emitted rather than elicited since there _____ (are or are no) observed eliciting stimuli.

28. If pressing the bar does not operate the food magazine, the response _____ reinforced.

29. Reinforcement makes responses more frequent while failure to receive reinforcement makes responses _____.

30. No eliciting stimuli are observed for bar pressing, flicking leaves in the park, etc. Therefore, responses of this type _____ (are or are not) classified as reflex behavior.

IDENTIFYING TYPES OF LEARNING

Paula is a five-year-old who plays easily with her many friends. Shyness has rarely been a problem, so her parents were surprised by what happened when they took her to a downtown department store at Christmas time to sit on Santa's knee.

When Paula and her parents went to the store, it was jammed with shoppers. People with large shopping bags were constantly bumping into Paula. When she and her parents got to where Santa was, they saw a long line of children and parents waiting. Several children in front of Paula were very tired and hungry. They cried loudly all the time they waited. When it was her turn to talk to Santa, Paula refused. She started to cry, and her parents spoke sternly to her. "We waited all this time for you! You need to talk to Santa now." Several adults in line behind Paula started to get angry and demanded that she either talk to Santa or get out of the way. Paula's parents decided that she was not ready for Santa right then. They picked her up and took her to a nearby ice cream shop to soothe her. They decided that there was no need to see Santa this Christmas. After ice cream, they passed by the Santa Claus line again, and Paula started to cry even though she knew she would not have to face Santa. For several days, the sight of Santas made Paula feel uneasy, but gradually her emotional reaction decreased to zero by Christmas Day.

Christmas turned out to be a good time for Paula. She had seen television ads for Baby Wonderful that made the doll look as though it was alive. When Paula would see a commercial for this doll, she would run to her mother and beg for it. Paula's mother at first did not want to spend so much money on a doll, but after many pleadings by Paula she gave in and told her, "I promise you will get Baby Wonderful." That stopped the pleading, and Paula was delighted when she opened a package with the doll inside on Christmas morning.

Later, on Christmas morning, Paula's father said she should call relatives and say thank you for the gifts she received in the mail. Before her first call, her father said, "I want you to say 'Thank you, Aunt Mary. I really love the slippers you sent. I'll use them this winter.' Try to remember what to say, Paula." When Paula got on the phone with Aunt Mary, she said, "Thanks. I like what you sent. Good-by." After she hung up, her father said, "That was okay, Paula, but on the next call I want you to be sure to name the gift. It will mean a lot to Uncle Ed that you say what you got, okay?" As the morning progressed, Paula improved at saying relatives' names and thanking them for specific gifts.

Materials: None

Procedure: Identify examples of (a) negative reinforcement, (b) classical conditioning, (c) shaping, (d) observational learning, (e) positive reinforcement, and (f) extinction.

Answer on your laboratory report form.

IDENTIFYING CLASSICAL, OPERANT, AND OBSERVATIONAL LEARNING – CONT.

Negative Reinforcement:

Paula was pleading for the "Baby Wonder" so her mom got it for her so she would stop crying.

Classical Conditioning:

When she walked by Santa & she started crying again.

Shaping:

When Paula's dad was telling her to call all her relatives thanking them for the specific gifts.

Observational Learning:

She started crying in the line b/c all the other kids were.

Positive Reinforcement:

Her mom asked her to stop nagging & she'll get what she wants.

Extinction:

walking away from Santa.

BEHAVIOR SHAPING EXERCISE

Behavior shaping is a process of learning. In behavior shaping, an animal (or human) gradually masters a complex behavior by trying many different behaviors, fine tuning reinforced behaviors, while gradually eliminating unreinforced behaviors. For example, when a lab rat is first placed in an operant conditioning chamber (or "Skinner Box"), the rat must learn, step-by-step, how to press the bar in order to get food reinforcement. That is, the rat is first rewarded for simply being near the lever, then for being near and facing the lever, then for being near, facing and touching the lever, and finally, for being near, facing, touching, and pressing the lever. Many human behaviors are also learned through behavior shaping. For example, when a toddler first begins to speak, parents reward any sounds that vaguely sound like talking. Then, the step-by-step process continues as the child gradually learns correct word usage, grammar, and pronunciation.

Materials: None

Procedure: 1. A student volunteer (or your instructor) will leave the classroom.

2. Then, the class will (1) determine the place in the room they will move the subject, and (2) determine the behavior(s) the subject will do at that place in the room.

3. Be creative in your choice of a target behavior. Consider selecting a target behavior which will require the subject to experiment with body, arm, leg, and head movements. For example, plan to have the subject move to one corner of the room and imitate a gorilla.

4. The class will also need to determine a form of reinforcement for the subject. No verbal (word) reinforcers will be allowed. For example, the subject might respond to brief bits of applause, or to the sound of a pen tapping on a desk.

5. After the class has determined the target behavior and reinforcer, the subject may enter the classroom.

6. As the subject moves about the room, the experimenters should reinforce only behavior that will eventually lead the subject to the target behavior.

BEHAVIOR SHAPING EXERCISE – CONT.

7. A note to the subject: After you master the location of your target behavior, you must experiment with a variety of bodily movements in order to figure out, step-by-step, what your target behavior is.

8. Repeat the exercise several times with a different target behavior.

Discussion Question:

In a paragraph essay, discuss an example from your own life experience illustrating behavior shaping. Identify the target behavior, the reinforcers which kept you working toward this behavior, and the process by which you eventually acquired the target behavior.

U N I T

8

Memory

SHORT TERM MEMORY

Psychologists believe when we are first learning new information that has just come into our memory through our senses, we have a component of memory that is very brief – short term memory.

In this experiment you will evaluate your own short term memory.

Materials: Cassette tape on short term memory (provided by your instructor).

Procedure: You will be taking a variety of word recall tests. Instructions will be given before each test.

Record all responses on your laboratory report form.

LABORATORY REPORT FORM: SHORT TERM MEMORY

Test 1 – Free Recall

1
2
3
4
5
6
7
8
9
10

How many words did you get correct?_____

Test 2 – Free Recall

1
2
3
4
5
6
7
8
9
10

How many words did you get correct?_____

Test 3 – Serial Recall

1
2
3
4
5
6
7
8
9
10

How many words did you get correct including order?_____

SHORT TERM MEMORY – CONT.

Test 4 – Serial Recall

1
2
3
4
5
6
7
8
9
10

How many words did you get correct including order?_____
What process did you use to remember the words and keep them in order?

Test 5 – Free Recall

1
2
3
4
5
6
7
8
9
10

How many words did you get correct?_____
Did you have any words from previous tests?

Test 6 – Subtract and Free Recall

Subtract 300	Recall	
		1
-7		2
		3
-7		4
		5
-7		6
		7
-7		8
		9
-7		10

How many words did you get correct?_____
How did the subtraction exercise effect your recall?

LONG TERM MEMORY (LEVELS OF PROCESSING)

There are various methods used by individuals to improve their long-term memory. In this experiment you will explore several methods and attain some insight into clues for improvement of your own memory.

Materials: Cassette Tape on long-term memory (provided by your instructor).

Procedure: You will receive specific instructions from your instructor. Be sure and use the laboratory report form provided.

Answer the summary question on your laboratory report form.

LABORATORY REPORT FORM – LONG TERM MEMORY

	Yes	No		Yes	No		Yes	No
1.			1.			1.		
2.			2.			2.		
3.			3.			3.		
4.			4.			4.		
5.			5.			5.		
6.			6.			6.		
7.			7.			7.		
8.			8.			8.		
9.			9.			9.		
10.			10.			10.		
11.			11.			11.		
12.			12.			12.		
13.			13.			13.		
14.			14.			14.		
15.			15.			15.		

Total   _____   _____   _____

LIST OF WORDS (RECALL)
Summary Question:

Based on these results, what can you do to improve your long-term memory?

INFORMATION TRANSMISSION – RUMORS REVISITED

Purpose: To investigate changes and distortions which occur with oral transmission of information.

Background:

What happens when you hear a "juicy" story and pass it on to a friend? Do you accurately reproduce the story or do you change it as you repeat it? Psychologists have discovered that certain interesting changes occur as information is passed orally from person to person.   Psychologists were particularly interested in this phenomenon during World War II when rumors occurred throughout the United States. Even today several cities have established rumor clinics where citizens can call and check the validity of any current rumor.

Materials: Story below.

Procedure: We will investigate how a story becomes distorted as it is passed among seven members of the class. The class will divide up into teams of seven who will sit together in the same row. The first person will read the story below (no one else is to read the story at this time!) and will then tell the story as accurately as possible to the person seated next to him/her. Immediately after doing so the first member will write down the story in as much detail as he/she can recall. This procedure is repeated for all seven members of the team.

Answer the summary questions on your laboratory report form.

Story:

A large muscular English professor who was dressed in his usual outfit of jeans and a wild sports shirt was walking across campus to teach his course in English literature. As he passed the campus lake he observed two older students from his morning class passionately making out in the shade of a large elm tree. As he continued across campus he met the dean of the graduate school who stopped to chat with him. She informed him that his application for a grant to study male chauvinism in Chaucer's poems was rejected because of a shortage of available funds. After debating somewhat violently the merits of his grant request the professor continued walking to his class. Upon reaching the class he discovered he had brought the wrong lecture note and consequently dismissed class for the day.

INFORMATION TRANSMISION – CONT.

During World War II professors Allport and Postman intensively investigated how information changes as it is passed from individual to individual. They found 3 major kinds of changes that occur:

1.   Leveling – as the story travels it becomes shorter and shorter.

2.   Sharpening – Certain aspects are emphasized and form the core of the story.

3.   Assimilation – Discrepant information is changed to conform to the core of the story, so that it seems more logical.

Results:

Record below the written version of the story as recalled by the last person in the team.

In addition you should read each written version of the story to see how the distortion came about. Be sure to go back and read the story as originally written.

Summary Questions:

1.   From the final story illustrate examples of leveling, sharpening, and assimilation.

2.   What happened in the length of the story as it was passed along?

3.   Did commonly held stereotypes affect recall of the story? How?

4.   What could be done to increase accuracy in this situation?

5.   Does this experiment accurately reproduce what occurs when a rumor spreads across campus? Why or why not?

UNIT

9

Intelligence

THE "DEBATE" GOES ON

One of the more controversial topics that we study in the field of psychology is the concept of intelligence. In this assignment, students will be assigned to groups to discuss/debate the critical issues revolving around the identification of intelligence.

Materials: None

Procedure: Within each group, please discuss the following issues:

1. What is your definition of intelligence, that is, what attributes define intelligence? What does intelligence measure?

2. What are the three most important characteristics or qualities that your group values in defining intelligence?

3. If you were to design a test of intelligence, how would you begin?

TRADITIONAL I.Q. TEST

Wanting to know how smart we are in comparison to others is often a topic we ponder. Standardized intelligence quotient tests were designed to answer this dilemma.

In this exercise you will be taking a standardized I.Q. test and also understanding the results of this test.

Materials: I.Q. Test

Procedure: Your instructor will give you the I.Q. test and answer form as well as further instructions.

Upon completion of the test your instructor will give you the results and explain their meaning.

Answer the summary questions on your laboratory report form

LABORATORY REPORT FORM: TRADITIONAL I.Q. TEST

Summary Questions:

1.   What do you think your score really means? Is it valid or not? Why?

2.   What did you think about the test items and what were considered correct answers? Explain.

CULTURE FAIR TEST

One of the biggest criticisms of standardized I.Q. tests is that they are unfair due to cultural bias. They seem to be designed specifically for white, middle to upper class people. Because of this bias several intelligence tests have been developed that attempt to eliminate cultural bias.

Materials: Raven's Progressive Matrices Test

Procedure: Your instructor will supply the test, answer form, as well as further instructions.

Upon completion your instructor will give you the results and interpretations.

Answer the summary questions on your laboratory report form.

LABORATORY REPORT FORM: CULTURE FAIR TEST

Summary Questions:

1. How were these results different or like the traditional I.Q. Test?

2. What do your results on this test mean?

3. Do you think they are valid? Why/why not?

4. What do you think about how it was graded and what answers were considered correct?

5. Which test do you think is a more valid measurement of your intelligence?

U N I T

10

Health Psychology

RELAXATION INDUCTION

Instructors can induce a mild state of relaxation in a short period of time. This activity can be useful to illustrate meditation and some of the preliminary feelings of hypnosis. In addition, rudimentary relaxation skills can assist students for whom test anxiety is a problem.

The following induction script takes about five minutes. It combines some features of Jacobson's (1964) deep muscle relaxation with autogenic training and visualization. The advantage of such a hybrid is that it increases the odds that some component of relaxation will "click" with the audience. In treatment, a much longer relaxation induction would be used. With practice, however, fairly deep relaxation can be attained in only a few minutes. Veteran mediators can get into an alpha state in only seconds!

Materials: Induction Script

Procedure: Before beginning the script, dim the room lights and tell students to put down their pens, uncross their legs, and put themselves in a comfortable position.

Read the following in a slow, smooth voice. Where there are three dots (...), pause for several seconds before reading the next statement.

We're going to start getting relaxed now. I want you to listen to what I say. It will be easier to get relaxed if you close your eyes now. Please close your eyes. Please tighten up your hands into fists. That's right. Feel the tension in your hands, wrists, and forearms. Hold it a few more seconds...Now open your fingers and let all the tension flow out...Notice the difference in the feeling between the tension that was there before and the relaxation that is growing now...Study the muscles and let them become more and more relaxed...Let the relaxation go even further.

  Clench your fists again now. Feel the tension. Hold it...Now try to touch your shoulders with your fists. Feel the tension all up your arms. Hold it...Study the muscles of your hands, arms, shoulders, and chest...Try to see the tension.

RELAXATION INDUCTION – CONT.

Now drop your arms and open your fingers...Let the tension just flow down and out your fingers. Try to see the tension flowing, dripping out of your fingers. Feel the difference between the tension that was there and the relaxation that is happening...Let the relaxation go even further than normal...That's good. Now concentrate on your breathing...Make your breathing slow and regular. Keep your mind on your breathing. As you breathe in through your nose, count slowly to four. That's right. Hold for a count of two. Now part your lips and exhale slowly through your mouth. Breathe as smoothly and as perfectly as you can...Each time you inhale, count slowly to four. Hold for two. Then part your lips and slowly exhale through your mouth...As you exhale, allow your body to relax completely. If your mind wanders, gently bring it back to your breathing...Each breath is a chance to get more relaxed...Very good...As you breathe out, think the word "relax." That's right, each breath means you can relax a bit more...Your whole body is calming down, feeling heavier and heavier. You are more relaxed with every breath...

Keep allowing the relaxation to go further. You can feel your shoulders becoming more relaxed...Your face is more relaxed...The muscles all over your body are smooth, calm, and quiet...Every time you exhale, you think "relax" and let all tension flow out. If your mind wanders, gently bring it back to your breathing and relaxation...

Now I want you to imagine yourself on a hill overlooking the ocean. You are sitting there, by yourself...Try to be there. See the water and the waves. The sky is blue with white, puffy clouds...Feel the breeze on your cheek, it is moving your hair. Feel the warm sun...You are completely alone and at peace here. Watch the waves coming in...The waves are in time with your breathing...As you breath with the waves, your body becomes even more relaxed...Enjoy this pleasant place...Visualize yourself in this restful place...Study and memorize this feeling, these surroundings. You can use it later when you need to create a relaxed state...Keep your mental eye on the waves and allow yourself to completely relax...Very good...

Unfortunately we must return to the world. We will do this slowly. I will count from four down to zero. At each number you will begin to move a bit more and at two slowly open your eyes. Four...Three...You can move a bit now...Two...slowly open your eyes...One...Zero. Welcome back. How do you feel?

STUDENT STRESS SCALE

The Student Stress Scale represents an adaptation of Holmes and Rahe's Social Readjustment Rating Scale. Each event is given a score that represents the amount of readjustment a person has to make in life as a result of the change. People with scores of 300 and higher have a high health risk. People scoring between 150 and 300 points have about a 50-50 chance of serious health change within two years. People scoring below 150 have a 1 in 3 chance of serious health change. Calculate your total Life Change Score (LCU) over the past year and then correlate this score with any changes in your health status.

Event	Life Change Unit
Death of a Close Family Member	100
Death of a Close Friend	73
Divorce Between Parents	65
Jail Term	63
Major Personal Injury or Illness	63
Marriage	58
Being Fired from Job	50
Failing an Important Course	47
Change in Health of Family Member	45
Pregnancy	45
Sex Problems	44
Serious Argument with Close Friend	40
Change in Financial Status	39
Change of Major	39
Trouble with Parents	39
New Girl-or Boyfriend	38
Increased Workload at School	37
Outstanding Personal Achievement	36
First Quarter/Semester in College	35
Change in Living Conditions	31
Serious Argument with Instructor	30
Lower Grades than Expected	29
Change in Sleeping Habits	29
Change in Social Activities	29
Change in Eating Habits	28
Chronic Car Trouble	26
Change in Number of Family Get-togethers	26
Too Many Missed Classes	25
Change of College	24
Dropping of More than One Class	23
Minor Traffic Violations	20

TOTAL _____

Stress Scale

Event	Life Change Unit
Death of a spouse	100
Divorce	73
Marital separation	65
Jail term	63
Death of a close family member	63
Personal injury or illness	53
Marriage	50
Fired at work	47
Marital reconciliation	45
Retirement	45
Change in health of family member	44
Pregnancy	40
Sex difficulties	39
Gain of new family member	39
Business readjustment	39
Change in financial state	38
Death of a close friend	37
Change to different line of work	36
Change in number of arguments with spouse	35
Mortgage over $100,000	31
Foreclosure of mortgage or loan	30
Change in responsibilities at work	29
Son or daughter leaving home	29
Trouble with in-laws	29
Outstanding personal achievement	28
Wife begins or stops work	26
Begin or end school	26
Change in living conditions	25
Revision of personal habits	24
Trouble with boss	23
Change in work hours or conditions	20
Change in residence	20
Change in schools	20
Change in recreation	19
Change in church activities	19
Change in social activities	18
Loan less than $10,000	17
Change in sleeping habits	16
Change in number of family get-togethers	15
Change in eating habits	15
Vacation	13
Christmas	12
Minor violations of law	11

TOTAL _____

STUDENT STRESS SCALE: LABORATORY REPORT FORM

Summary Questions:

1. How does your individual score on the scale compare with the guidelines for health related problems?

2. Do you think your score truly reflects your own perception of the impact of stress in your life?

3. Based on the score and your perception of the score, do you feel that there is a need for changing your lifestyle in order to better manage stress in your life?

4. Describe your reaction to these scales that equate stress with health conditions. Can psychologists predict future health problems through an association with stress?

UNIT

11

Developmental

ANDROGYNY

Androgyny refers to the capacity of men and women to be both masculine and feminine in their attitudes and behavior. For example a person can be both tough and tender, compassionate and strong, ambitious and sensitive to the needs of others. A person who successfully integrates both traditional male and female gender roles is said to be androgynous.

There is a great deal of debate among psychologists as to whether androgyny should be the goal of personality development in all individuals. Most research points out that androgynous individuals do seem to adapt more quickly and successfully, but androgyny does not solve all problems or guarantee more perfect relationships.

In this study you will explore androgyny on a personal level.

Materials: Androgyny Scale

Procedure: Upon completion of the inventory you will be given instructions on how to score the inventory and how to interpret these results.

Answer the questions on your laboratory report form(s).

ANDROGYNY SCALE

Listed below are a number of personality characteristics. Use these to describe yourself. On the Androgyny Scale Scoring Form, indicate a scale of 1 to 5, how true of you these characteristics are. Do not leave any unmarked.

Column A	Column B	Column C
1. independent	2. dependable	3. productive
4. logical	5. obliging	6. commiserating
7. defends own	8. envious	9. merry beliefs
10. has leadership abilities	11. temperamental	12. sensitive to the needs of others
13. autonomous	14. honest	15. bashful
16. willing to take chances	17. scrupulous	18. sympathetic
19. robust	20. reticent	21. loving
22. makes decisions easily	23. Dramatic	24. tender
25. confident	26. genuine	27. flatterable
28. cheerful	29. self-sufficient	30. powerful personality
31. eager to soothe hurt feelings	32. faithful	33. self-important
34. unpredictable	35. controlling	36. commanding
37. soft-spoken	38. feminine	39. amiable
40. versatile	41. masculine	42. individualistic
43. gracious harsh language	44. does not use	45. grave
46. unsystematic	47. willing to take a stand	48. competitive
49. kindhearted	50. loves children	51. sociable
52. tactful	53. aggressive	54. aspiring
55. trusting	56. gentle	57. inefficient
58. traditional	59. acts as a leader	60. childlike

ANDROGYNY SCALE SCORING FORM

1	2	3	4	5
never true	sometimes true	occasionally true	often true	always true

Column A	Column B	Column C
1. 1 2 3 4 5	2. 1 2 3 4 5	3. 1 2 3 4 5
4. 1 2 3 4 5	5. 1 2 3 4 5	6. 1 2 3 4 5
7. 1 2 3 4 5	8. 1 2 3 4 5	9. 1 2 3 4 5
10. 1 2 3 4 5	11. 1 2 3 4 5	12. 1 2 3 4 5
13. 1 2 3 4 5	14. 1 2 3 4 5	15. 1 2 3 4 5
16. 1 2 3 4 5	17. 1 2 3 4 5	18. 1 2 3 4 5
19. 1 2 3 4 5	20. 1 2 3 4 5	21. 1 2 3 4 5
22. 1 2 3 4 5	23. 1 2 3 4 5	24. 1 2 3 4 5
25. 1 2 3 4 5	26. 1 2 3 4 5	27. 1 2 3 4 5
28. 1 2 3 4 5	29. 1 2 3 4 5	30. 1 2 3 4 5
31. 1 2 3 4 5	32. 1 2 3 4 5	33. 1 2 3 4 5
34. 1 2 3 4 5	35. 1 2 3 4 5	36. 1 2 3 4 5
37. 1 2 3 4 5	38. 1 2 3 4 5	39. 1 2 3 4 5
40. 1 2 3 4 5	41. 1 2 3 4 5	42. 1 2 3 4 5
43. 1 2 3 4 5	44. 1 2 3 4 5	45. 1 2 3 4 5
46. 1 2 3 4 5	47. 1 2 3 4 5	48. 1 2 3 4 5
49. 1 2 3 4 5	50. 1 2 3 4 5	51. 1 2 3 4 5
52. 1 2 3 4 5	53. 1 2 3 4 5	54. 1 2 3 4 5
55. 1 2 3 4 5	56. 1 2 3 4 5	57. 1 2 3 4 5
58. 1 2 3 4 5	59. 1 2 3 4 5	60. 1 2 3 4 5

A = _____   B = _____

ANDROGYNY SCALE

Scoring Instructions

Of the preceding 60 personality characteristics listed, 20 are commonly thought of as masculine (ambitious, assertive, independent, etc.), 20 are feminine (affectionate, gentle, understanding, etc.), and 20 are neutral (truthful, likable, etc.). On the basis of your answers you are to receive three major scores: A Masculinity Score, a Femininity Score, and an Androgyny score. To compute the Masculinity Score, add up all of the points in column A. Divide that sum by 20. To compute the Femininity score, add up all of the points in column B. Divide that sum by 20. If your Masculinity Score is above 3.5 and your Femininity Score is above 3.5, then you would be classified as Androgynous on Bem's Scale.

Scoring:

Column A = _____ divided by 20 = _____ Masculinity score

Column B = _____ divided by 20 = _____ Femininity score

To be Androgynous:

    the Masculinity score must be greater than 3.5
    or the Femininity score must be greater than 3.5

LABORATORY REPORT FORM: ANDROGYNY

Summary Questions:

1.   What does your score mean?

2.   Were you surprised with these results? Why?

3.   Examine the personality characteristics. Do you agree with Dr. Bem on the labeling of certain characteristics as masculine or feminine?

4.   Give specific examples to substantiate your answer to question 3.

BASIC LIFE EXPECTANCY

Materials: Basic Life Expectancy Questionnaire

Procedure: Decide how each item below applies to you and add or subtract the appropriate number of years from your basic life expectancy.

Answer the summary questions on your laboratory report form(s).

1. Family history
    Add five years if two or more of your grandparents live to 80 or beyond.
    Subtract four years if any parent, grandparent, sister, or brother died of heart attack or stroke before 50.
    Subtract two years if anyone died from these diseases before 60.
    Subtract three years for each case of diabetes, thyroid disorder, breast cancer, cancer of the digestive system, asthma, or chronic bronchitis among parents or grandparents.

2. Marital status
    If you are married, add four years.
    If you are over twenty-five and not married, subtract one year for every unwedded decade.

3. Economic status
    Add two years if your family income is over $60,000 per year.
    Subtract three years if you have been poor for the greater part of your life.

4. Physique
    Subtract one year for every ten pounds you are overweight.
    For each inch your girth measurement exceeds your chest measurement, deduct two years.
    Add three years if you are over forty and not overweight.

5. Exercise
    Add three years if you exercise regularly and moderately (jogging three times a week).
    Add five years if you exercise regularly and vigorously (long-distance running three times a week.)
    Subtract three years if your job is sedentary
    Add three years if your job is active.

BASIC LIFE EXPECTANCY – CONT.

6.   Alcohol
      Add two years if you are a light drinker.
      (one or three drinks a week).
      Subtract one year if you are a teetotaler.

7.   Smoking
      Subtract eight years if you smoke two or
      more packs of cigarettes per day.
      Subtract two years if you smoke one to two
      packs per day.
      Subtract two years if you smoke less than
      one pack.
      Subtract two years if you regularly smoke
      a pipe or cigars.

8.   Disposition
      Add two years if you a reasoned, practical
      person.
      Subtract two years if you are aggressive,
      intense, and competitive.
      Add one to five years if you are basically
      and content with life.
      Subtract one to five years if you are often
      unhappy, worried, and often feel guilty.

9.   Education
      Subtract two years if you have less than a
      high school education.
      Add one year if you attended four years of
      school beyond high school.
      Add three years if you attended five or more
      years beyond high school.

10.   Environment
      Add four years if you have lived most of
      your life in a rural environment.
      Subtract two years if you have lived most
      of your life in an urban environment.

11.   Sleep
      Subtract five years if you sleep more than
      nine hours a day.

12.   Temperature
      Add two years if your home's thermostat is
      set at no more than 68 F.

13.   Health Care
      Add three years if you have regular medical
      checkups and regular dental care.
      Subtract two years if you are frequently
      ill.

Your Life Expectancy Total

LABORATORY REPORT FORM: BASIC LIFE EXPECTANCY

Average male life expectancy = 70

Average female life expectancy = 75

Write down your average life expectancy based totally upon whether you are male or female.

_____ years average life expectancy.

 + 10 yrs. if you are in your 50's or 60's

 + 2 yrs. if you are over 60

_____ yrs. subtotal

Now use this subtotal to add or subtract the points on this test.

Your life expectancy _____ yrs.

Summary Questions:

1.   What factors are adding to your longevity?

2.   What factors are subtracting years?

3.   Which of these factors surprised or concerned you? Why?

CHILDREN'S APPERCEPTION TEST

The Children's Apperception Test, a projective psychological test, was designed to facilitate an understanding of a child's relationship to his/her most important figures and drives. The subject is shown a series of cards and is asked to tell a story about each. The examiner then interprets these responses using specific test criteria.

Materials: Children's Apperception Test
                  Transcript of subject's responses

Procedure: You will be shown a series of pictures and will read an anonymous subject's responses to each of these pictures. Choose four stories to analyze using your laboratory report form.

Answer the questions on your laboratory report form(s).

CHILDREN'S APPERCEPTION TEST TRANSCRIPT

Subject (S):   6 year old female

Experimenter (E):   We are going to play a game. I'm going to show you several pictures and I would like you to tell me a story about each picture. The story should have a beginning, middle, and end. Also, please tell me how the characters are feeling and what they are doing.

Subject interrupts

Experimenter: Yes, do have a question?

Subject: Do you tell the story first, or do you tell what the animals are doing and what's happening in the picture?

E: Your story should include what the animals are doing and what is happening in the picture. Are you ready to begin?

S: Yes.

E: Picture number one.

S: One day three baby chickens were eating porridge and the mother hen was watching them or should I say standing by. Then one of them got up and said, "I'm going to go out into the meadow." The others said, "We'll join you after we finish." Then the mother hen said to the one who was named Billy who wanted to go out in the field...and she said, "Wait for me and would you please wait for the others?" Then Billy sat down and waited.

E: Anything else?

S: and then the other two finished...and the mother hen said, "I'll be out on the front porch watching." So they all went and played some games. Can I say the end?

E: You bet!

S: The end.

E: Are you ready for picture 2?

S: Yes. Three bears were playing tug-a-war one day and there was one on one team and two on the other. Then one of 'em stopped and they said I wanna play another game. So the other two stopped and before they started to play the new game, the mother asked, "Who won?" The daddy bear said, "I think we should say that it was a tie." So they went on to the next game. All they had to play with was with rope because they forgot to bring their toys. They have some toys, but you can't play with them in these games. Next they were going to skip rope, and so the mother bear and the father bear held the end of the rope. Then baby bear jumped.   Then it was the papa bear's turn and it was the mother bear's turn, and then it went around and around. Then the baby bear said, "I want to play another game."   And then the baby bear asked before they started to play that game, "Who won?" And then the bear said, "I think you won, little one."   And then next they were going to play "make a basket," and what they are going to do is cut the ropes, get some sticks, and start making out what they think will look like a basket. The end.

E: Ready for picture 3?

S: One day the lion was sitting in his big chair, and he was sitting there and he was bored.   So he asked the little mouse, "Would you play a game with me?" And the mouse said, "Sure." So they played a game of marbles so the mouse wouldn't feel out of the game because he was so small. They played that for a while and then the lion said, "I'm getting tired of this game. Why don't we play tug-a-war?" So they got a little piece of string so the mouse could play, and they started tugging. The lion had fun with this for about 2 hours. Then he said, "Thank you, little mouse. I think I have some other ideas that one can play."   So he started to play skipping rope, and he had fun with that. Then he sat in his big chair and took a nap. The end.

E: Ready for picture 4?

S: One day the kangaroo family was taking a picnic to the woods and the biggest was riding a bike. And the mother was going to the park for the picnic, and all the others--the two other kangaroos--thought that was a fine idea. So they went to the park, and then they sat down for a minute. Then they heard rattling in the woods that was by the park. So the mother said, "Wait right here. I'm going to go see what that was." When she was gone and it was quiet, someone came up and grabbed the two kangaroos that were sitting on the picnic quilt. And then he took them to a house, and it was a log house. And then the mother came back and she said, "Where is Fred, the biggest, and where is John, the littlest?" And so they went looking. Then the mother said, "I've heard of this kidnapper who's in the woods by the park, and he lives in a log cabin. So let's check there." So they went there and sure enough there they were. And she said, "I'm going to be going with my two children. Goodbye." The end.

E: This is card number 5.

S: One day the two little bears were sleeping one night. And then one woke up and woke the other up and said, "Let's talk."   So they were whispering to each other. The time was about quarter 'til twelve, so they had slept a good while. And then their mama and papa bear were downstairs because they were getting a midnight snack. So the baby bear said, "Let's get out of our crib, and we'll go down and say hello to mama bear and papa bear." So they did just that. And then mama bear said, "You scurry up to bed now." So they went back to bed and they went to sleep. The end.

E: Card number 6.

S: Three bears were hibernating in a cave. And papa bear said, "I'm getting hungry." Of course, the other two were just sound asleep. So the papa bear said, "I'll go get some fish." So he went out and he got some fish and he ate the fish and said, "Those were so good." And he said, "How would you like me to get you a fish dinner tonight?" So the other two said, "Okay." Because they were so tired. So he went and got ten fish for the whole family. And he came back and he said, "These are the goodest I could get." So they said, "These are fine." So they were eating their dinner. And then he said, "I think when I finish dinner, I think I'm gonna go straight to bed." Of course it was winter time, and they had no place to walk around and go, so they just went back to sleep. And then someone knocked at the door, and so the papa bear answered it. It was the mail bear. And the mail bear said, "It's sure cold out there. I wondered if I could stay with you." They said, "Of course." And they had a happy night. The end.

E: Card number 7.

S: One night a tiger came after a monkey. And the tiger was really nice, but he thought the monkey was in his territory. So he went out after the monkey. And the monkey said, "Help!" But the lion said, " Well, you were in my territory." "Well, I didn't mean to Mr. Lion." So the tiger said to the monkey, "Okay, you can go now." So of course he was a very nice lion. And then he said, "I wonder what I can have for breakfast?" So (laughs) he went out to investigate for some deer that he could get. So he got an antelope instead of a deer because he gets confused of those two. So he ate that and said, "That's very good." So then he took an afternoon nap. Then he got up and said, "What's there to eat for lunch?" So he said, "I would like a monkey to eat."   (Laughs) This is really a strange lion. So he went out and got a monkey; it wasn't the monkey who trespassed, okay. So the tiger ate that monkey. Then he said, "I think I'm going to take a walk." So he took his walk, about 5 miles, because he needed to run. So he ran five mile each day. Then he said, "What is there to eat for dinner?" So he got out and said, "I think I'll eat. . . let's see, I think I'll go to town." And of course animals were in this town, since he was walking in a street-like jungle. So he went to town. "I think I'll try some food in the town." So he got a nice chicken dinner, and then he went to the candy shop and got some candy for dessert. The end.

E: This is card number 8.

S: The monkey family was talking and whispering, and they were having a pleasant time that afternoon. So then the baby monkey, or should I say child monkey, went out and he got his mother's permission. So he went out into the front yard, and he played and played and played. Then his friend came over and said, "Can I play with you?" "Did your mother say you could?" And the friend said, "No." Then the monkey said, "Well, go back and tell her that you're going to be over at my house for a few minutes and could you come play." So he checked out with his mother and his mother said, "Yes." Then he checked with his mother, and his mother said, "Okay."   So they started to play tug-a-war. And then the monkey said, "I think I'll go in." So he went in and sat on the couch with his brother and sister. And his mother said, "Did you have fun?" Then he said, "Yes." And then he said, "Do you need to leave?" And the friend said, "No." And he said, "Come to my room and we'll play in there." So they started playing a battleship game. So the friend said, "I think I'll go now." The monkey went and ate dinner, and the monkey went to bed because he was really tired because his friend came over. The end.

LABORATORY REPORT FORM: CHILDREN'S APPERCEPTION TEST

Summarize:

	Story #1	Story #2
1. Main theme		
2. Main needs and drives of hero		
3. Conception of environment (world) as:		
4. Parental figures are seen as _____ Contemporary figures are seen as____ Junior figures are seen as _____		
5. Significant conflicts:		
6. Nature of anxieties:		
7. Main defenses against conflicts and fears:		
8. Adequacy of superego as manifested by "punishment" for crime being: appropriate_____ inappropriate_____ too severe_____ inconsistent_____		
9. Integration of the ego, manifesting itself in: Hero: adequate_____ inadequate_____ Outcome: happy_____ unhappy_____ realistic_____ unrealistic_____		

LABORATORY REPORT FORM: CHILDREN'S APPERCEPTION TEST

Summarize:

	Story #3	Story #4
1. Main theme		
2. Main needs and drives of hero		
3. Conception of environment (world) as:		
4. Parental figures are seen as _____ Contemporary figures are seen as____ Junior figures are seen as _____		
5. Significant conflicts:		
6. Nature of anxieties:		
7. Main defenses against conflicts and fears:		
8. Adequacy of superego as manifested by "punishment" for crime being: appropriate_____ inappropriate_____ too severe_____ inconsistent_____		
9. Integration of the ego, manifesting itself in: Hero: adequate_____ inadequate_____ Outcome: happy_____ unhappy_____ realistic_____ unrealistic_____		

LABORATORY REPORT FORM: CHILDREN'S APPERCEPTION TEST

Summary Questions:

1.   What do the test responses reveal about this child?

2.   Discuss the relationship of psychoanalytic theory of personality development to the design of the test materials and the method of interpreting test responses.

3.   What is your opinion about this testing method and its usefulness in obtaining information about needs and drives?

UNIT

12 Personality

IDENTIFYING DEFENSE MECHANISMS

According to Sigmund Freud, people use defense mechanisms to cope with the conflict that exists between the desires of the id and the perfectionistic demands of the superego. Defense mechanisms serve the ego, and used in moderation are considered useful. When overused, being "defensive" contributes to dysfunction.

Materials: Questionnaire in Lab Manual

Procedure: Listed below are examples of behaviors that typify specific defense mechanisms. Using the definitions of defense mechanisms provided, identify the one that is most appropriate to the given behavior in each example. Some behaviors do not typify defense mechanisms and should be noted as N/A (not applicable).

_____ 1.   John thought that almost everyone but himself was cheating on the psychology exam.

_____ 2.   Lisa was embarrassed when she kept forgetting her appointment with the dentist.

_____ 3.   Although Joan had not been very close to her mother during her childhood she was now so oversolicitous of her mother's health and comfort that she was finding her own marriage being threatened.

_____ 4.   After her new baby brother came home from the hospital the parents discovered Cheryl had dismembered her favorite doll.

_____ 5.   A student attributes his flunking out of the university to the poor quality of teaching there.

_____ 6.   Through incredible hard work and perseverance, the 50-year old woman, who had never had a sexual relationship, became a famous artist.

_____ 7.   A man who has had many extramarital affairs begins to accuse his wife of being unfaithful.

IDENTIFYING DEFENSE MECHANISM – CONT.

_____ 8.   Tommy began wetting his pants again after the birth of his baby brother.

_____ 9.   Michael looked at the grade that was posted for his math course and told his friend that the professor must have made a mistake in calculating the grade because it could not be correct.

_____ 10.   Chuck became extremely nervous during college exams and sweated profusely.

_____ 11.   Two years after breaking off his relationship with Julie, Rick fails to even recognize her at a cocktail party.

_____ 12.   A mother spanks her child too often because she says it will teach him right from wrong.

_____ 13.   Mark slams the door to the classroom after failing the exam.

_____ 14.   After an unsuccessful attempt at a sexual relationship, Tim began devoting most of his energies toward church activities.

_____ 15.   Patrick broke off his relationship with Susan but Susan still talks as if they continue to date each other.

_____ 16.   The "old maid" looked under her bed every night fearing a man might be hiding there.

_____ 17.   Paula reduced her anxiety about her physics exam by studying twice as long as necessary.

Reaction Formation	A defense against a threatening impulse, involving actively expressing the opposite impulse.
Repression	The ego-defense mechanism whereby threatening or painful thoughts or feelings are excluded from awareness.
Projection	Attributing to others one's own unacceptable desires and impulses.
Displacement	Discharge impulses by shifting from a threatening object to a "safer target."
Rationalization	Involves explaining away failures or losses.
Sublimation	A redirection of sexual or aggressive energy into creative behaviors.
Regression	Reverting to a form of behavior that one has outgrown, usually to an earlier phase of development where the demands were not so great.
Denial	A way of distorting what the individual thinks, feels, or perceives in a traumatic situation.

SENTENCE COMPLETION

In this exercise you will experience how a projective personality test can be used to gain insight into an individual's personality.

In some personality assessment instruments, you project your personality on to the test. There are no right or wrong answers, and no answers to choose from.

Materials: Sentence Completion Test

Procedure: Complete each sentence with the first thought that comes into your mind. It can be one word or several phrases. Be honest – you will not hand in this part of the exercise. Score your responses.

Answer the summary questions on your laboratory report form(s).

1. Higher education

2. My best friend

3. I secretly wish

4. Sex

5. My family

6. Sometimes I

7. Getting married

8. Compared to my friends, I

9. Mom

10. What worries me is

11. I feel like

SENTENCE COMPLETION – CONT.

12. My biggest wish

13. When I was younger

14. My father and I

15. My looks are

16. In the evening

17. I fear

18. My college courses

19. My dad thinks my mom

20. I really hope

21. The opposite sex

22. My best friend doesn't know

23. My mom

24. I get angry when

25. A decade from now I

26. It is hard for me to

27. Even though it is silly

28. Women

29. My nerves

30. I want

31. I have fantasies about

32. My dad

33. The thing that bothers me most about myself is

34. I would eventually like to

SENTENCE COMPLETION – CONT.

35. Mothers should

36. Secretly I need

37. Many of my friends

38. Going on dates

39. A friend

40. For sure

41. I wish I could forget

42. My mom thinks my dad

43. People

44. Tomorrow

45. I don't know why

46. After I'm married

47. My mother and I

48. My dream

49. If only I could

50. I would be truly happy if

LABORATORY REPORT FORM – SENTENCE COMPLETION

Scoring: You are to go back and evaluate each of the statements you completed. Put one of the following letters beside each sentence.

P = Sentence is humorous, happy, positive, successful, goal-oriented, friendly, etc.

N =   Sentence is pessimistic, shows rejection, unhappy, failure, negative, shows conflict.

B = Sentence is a statement of fact or neutral.
        EX. – Men are the opposite sex.

Now get a total for each letter.

P =

N =

B =

Take you N score and add 50 to it.

        N

        +50

Now subtract your P score from this total.

        N

        +50

        – P

This is your score for the test.

Total Score = _____

SENTENCE COMPLETION: LABORATORY REPORT FORM

What Your Score Means:

Scores can be from 0 to 100. A score of 50 or below indicates you generally have a positive outlook on life, feel you will be successful at what you attempt, and if you fail you will learn from mistakes, an overall optimistic.

If you score is 50 or above it suggests that you underestimate your abilities, and are somewhat pessimistic. (This does not mean psychological maladjustment – just your way of viewing your life). Probably a perfectionist.

Now go back through your sentences and read all the ones that have to do with (1) your mother (9, 23, 35, 42); (2) your father (14, 19, 32); (3) sex, and marriage (4, 7, 21, 38, 46); (4) future (3, 12, 20, 25, 30, 34, 44, 48, 50).

Summary Questions:

Describe themes you see about:

1. Your mother

2. Your father

3. Sex and marriage

4. Future goal

5. If a stranger were to read your responses, what general conclusions would this person draw about your personality?

MYERS-BRIGGS TYPE INDICATOR

Psychologists have developed a wide variety of techniques to help understand or assess people's personalities.

One classification of techniques is referred to as the objective personality assessment test. In these assessments you must choose one answer from those presented.

In this project you will be taking an objective personality assessment which is based on Carl Jung's theory of personality. You will discover certain elements of your personality as defined by Jung.

Materials: Myers-Briggs Type Indicator

Procedure: Answer questions on the sheet provided by your instructor. Score the test, arriving at a four-letter code. Pick up a profile sheet matching your code from your instructor. Read the description of your personality type.

Answer the summary questions on your laboratory report form(s).

LABORATORY REPORT FORM: MYERS BRIGGS

Summary Questions:

1.   State your personality type._____ _____ _____ _____

2.   Explain what each of the four letters in your personality type means.

LABORATORY REPORT FORM: MYERS BRIGGS – CONT.

3.   According to the results, which of the four letters is your most dominant characteristic? Which is the least dominant for you?

4.   After reading your profile, identify and discuss several characteristics which fit you very well. Give a specific example of a life experience which supports this characteristic for each.

5.   After reading your profile, identify and discuss any characteristic which does not fit you well. Give a specific example of a life experience which invalidates this characteristic.

THEMATIC APPERCEPTION TEST

The Thematic Apperception Test, commonly known as the TAT, is a method of revealing to a trained interpreter some of the drives, emotions, and conflicts of personality. Originally developed in 1936 by Henry Murray and his staff, the revised TAT is still widely used by psychologists as a projective personality test.

Materials: Thematic Apperception Test
Audio tape with subject responses

Procedure: You will be shown a series of pictures and will listen to an anonymous subject's responses to each of these pictures.

Answer the questions on your laboratory report form(s).

Thematic Apperception Test – Transcript

Subject: Male 24

Experimenter (E):   This is the test protocol for the Thematic Apperception Test. This is a test of imagination, one form of intelligence. I'm going to show you some pictures one at a time and your task will be to make up a story about each one. Tell what led up to the event shown in the picture, describe what's happening at the moment, what the characters are feeling and thinking, and then give the outcome. Speak your thoughts as they come to your mind. Do you understand?

Subject (S):   I understand.

E: We will begin with card 18 BM

S: With this picture it looks like the man is apparently in pain, like somebody's holding him back off the edge. Somebody's holding him back. Maybe some trials in his life have depressed him and now he's feeling a little bit relaxed.

E: This is card 13 B

S: It looks like in this picture that maybe it's like a poor family, maybe in the 50's or 60's. Maybe a guy driving through decided to stop by and take a picture. He just thought that this would make a great picture. The little boy is looking pretty sad, but at the same time kind of happy because someone is taking the time out to spend time with him.

E: Next is 9 BM

S: With this picture, it looks like these guys are out after an all-night-drunk. It looks like they might have gone out and partied a little bit and ended up spending the night out in the field. They look pretty content.

E: This is 7 BM

S: With this picture, it looks like it's a father-son portrait to me. It looks like they're discussing something; maybe the dad is trying to spread a little bit of wisdom to his son. His son is trying to take it all in, the feelings of caring on the dad's part. He is trying to understand where the dad's coming from.

E: Card 6 BM

S: The guy just delivered some devastating news to a mother or grandmother. There are feelings of sadness and maybe intrigue. They don't know what to think. And it looks like they both have some thinking to do.

E: This is card 5

S: It looks like the mom's popping in to tell the kids that dinner is ready. There's a little bit of sternness in her and authority.

E: Card 4

S: It looks like a picture from a movie. They're trying to discuss some relationship problems. Maybe he's not understanding, and she's trying to get him to understand, and he's pulling away.

E: Card 2

S: This looks like a Michelangelo painting. Maybe the lady is looking back on her life. The guy with the horse is her husband representing the middle part of her life. Maybe she is looking forward to her grandparent years.

E: Card 1

S: It looks like this little boy is bored. Apparently he's not too enthusiastic about taking his violin lessons. Maybe he really wants to, or maybe he just being defiant. I'm not sure. Afterward he picks it up because they make him take the lessons.

E: Number 20

S: It looks like a late night picture. The emotion of solitude or deep thinking. The guy is just walking home from a long day at work, just thinking about his life, just thinking that he can't wait to get home to his family.

(Revisited) he's walking because he lives in the city...just chose to walk home that night...just to give in some serious thought into how his life is going...after the first part of his walk he was thinking that this is kind of silly I could just get into the car...he's thankful that everything is going well in his life..

Subject: Female 26

Card 13 MF

S: The woman in this picture came in to this apartment and she is dead or dying. This is not her place of residence; it is the man in the pictures' place of residence. She came to his apartment because she knew that she was failing in health, and she was about to die. And he wasn't there when she got there, so she lay on the bed and was resting. When the man came in to find her, she is almost gone. His reaction to her is one of...He is very sad because she about to die and he loves this woman. He knows that he has to call the authorities and have her body taken away. She doesn't have any family for him to contact that he knows of, so he is the sole mourner at her funeral.

Card 10

S: This young woman is a spy, and the older woman in the picture is her confidant or someone she is passing information to in order to get information to someone else. They are in a small village in the Balkans, and this young woman is hiding from people, and she sneaks into the older woman's house to pass her this important information. The older woman is actually in disguise; she's actually a man in an older woman's disguise so as to not be caught. The older woman takes the information and leaves the country with the information to be passed on.

E: Talk a little about what the characters in your story might be thinking and feeling.

S: The feeling, of course is fear, but also anticipation and excitement for doing something illegal. They are exhilarated as well as fearful, but they trust one another so that's not an issue here. The young woman is thinking about how she can get back out and into safety without being discovered. While the older woman is excited about getting out of the country, knowing that she'll be safe.

Card 16

E: Your last card is a little bit different. I want you to see what you can see on this blank card and describe it to me in detail.

S: I imagine the great pyramids, and they are lined up side by side. They are magnificent in detail and so uniform in their shape and so perfect in their shape, it is almost as though you could cut something on the lines. They are ivory in color, almost like they're marble or alabaster, and they are shining with gold, silver and jewels all around them, and there's nothing else. There's water to the side of them and desert all around them. So it is just three pyramids lined up. It is sunset, so it is almost as though they are glowing because of the position of the sun and the gold and silver, the metal on the pyramids.

E: Now tell me a story about what you just described.

S: I imagine that there is a boat coming up the side on the waterway that is to the right of the pyramids. People are getting off the boat, but they are today's people (modern), but yet the pyramids are very different, and they have an appearance that is very different than it should be, as though they hadn't aged at all. The people, most of which are Egyptian people, are walking up to the pyramids. These are tour guides and people on camels. People are being transported from the boat to the pyramids, just as if it happened everyday. From a distance it looks like the pyramids look different, but they think, "Okay, it's morning time now." So they think, "Well it's just the way the sun is hitting it." But as they get closer to the pyramids they see that they are looking at the original state of the pyramids.

LABORATORY REPORT FORM: THEMATIC APPERCEPTION TEST

Summarize:

	Story #1	Story #2
1. Main theme		
2. Main needs and drives of hero		
3. Conception of environment (world) as:		
4. Parental figures are seen as _____ Contemporary figures are seen as_____ Junior figures are seen as _____		
5. Significant conflicts:		
6. Nature of anxieties:		
7. Main defenses against conflicts and fears:		
8. Adequacy of superego as manifested by "punishment" for crime being: appropriate_____ inappropriate_____ too severe_____ inconsistent_____		
9. Integration of the ego, manifesting itself in: Hero: adequate_____ inadequate_____ Outcome: happy_____ unhappy_____ realistic_____ unrealistic_____		

LABORATORY REPORT FORM: THEMATIC APPERCEPTION TEST

Summarize:

	Story #3	Story #4
1. Main theme		
2. Main needs and drives of hero		
3. Conception of environment (world) as:		
4. Parental figures are seen as _____ Contemporary figures are seen as____ Junior figures are seen as _____		
5. Significant conflicts:		
6. Nature of anxieties:		
7. Main defenses against conflicts and fears:		
8. Adequacy of superego as manifested by "punishment" for crime being: appropriate_____ inappropriate_____ too severe_____ inconsistent_____		
9. Integration of the ego, manifesting itself in: Hero: adequate_____ inadequate_____ Outcome: happy_____ unhappy_____ realistic_____ unrealistic_____		

LABORATORY REPORT FORM: THEMATIC APPERCEPTION TEST

Summary Questions:

1. What do the test responses reveal about this person?

2. What is your opinion about this testing method and its usefulness in obtaining information about needs and drives?

UNIT

13

Psychological
Disorders

THREE APPROACHES TO PSYCHOTHERAPY

Treatment for psychological disorders often includes some type of therapy. Psychotherapy describes treatments designed to help people resolve behavioral, emotional, and interpersonal problems and improve the quality of their lives.

Materials: "Gloria" videotape, with segments from therapy sessions with Carl Rogers (Client-Centered Therapy), Fritz Perls (Gestalt Therapy), and Albert Ellis (Rational-Emotive Therapy).

Procedure: You will view the "Gloria" tape and complete the Laboratory Report Form.

Answer the summary questions on your laboratory report form(s).

LABORATORY REPORT FORM – THREE APPROACHES TO PSYCHOTHERAPY

Summary Questions:

1.   What common problems were addressed by all three psychotherapies?

2.   Which therapy was most effective with Gloria? Please explain your answer.

3.   What type of therapy do you believe would be most effective for you? Explain your response.

DIAGNOSING MENTAL DISORDERS

The most widely used classification system for abnormal behavior patterns is the Diagnostic and Statistical Manual of Mental Disorders. In order to familiarize you with the diagnostic procedure, you will view a series of psychiatric interviews and will attempt to make a diagnosis of the mental disorder portrayed.

Materials: Videotape of clinical vignettes.

Procedure: 1. The instructor will assign each student to a small group.

2. Students will view a series of clinical vignettes.

3. Each group will work together to answer questions on the laboratory report form.

4. Each group member will turn in a completed laboratory report form

LABORATORY REPORT FORM: DIAGNOSING MENTAL DISORDERS

Complete the following information:

Vignette #1:

Client's name_____

Clinical diagnosis_____

Describe the most striking behaviors exhibited by the client, as well as other information provided in the psychiatric interview, that led you to make your diagnosis:

_____

_____

_____

_____

Vignette #2:

Client's name_____

Clinical diagnosis_____

Describe the most striking behaviors exhibited by the client, as well as other information provided in the psychiatric interview, that led you to make your diagnosis:

_____

_____

_____

_____

LABORATORY REPORT FORM: DIAGNOSING MENTAL DISORDERS – CONT.

Vignette #3:

      Client's name_____

      Clinical diagnosis_____

Describe the most striking behaviors exhibited by the client, as well as other information provided in the psychiatric interview, that led you to make your diagnosis:

_____

_____

_____

_____

Vignette #4:

      Client's name_____

      Clinical diagnosis_____

Describe the most striking behaviors exhibited by the client, as well as other information provided in the psychiatric interview, that led you to make your diagnosis:

_____

_____

_____

_____

LABORATORY REPORT FORM: DIAGNOSING MENTAL DISORDERS – CONT.

Vignette #5:

    Client's name_____

    Clinical diagnosis_____

    Describe the most striking behaviors exhibited by the client, as well as other information provided in the psychiatric interview, that led you to make your diagnosis:

_____

_____

_____

_____

UNIT

14

Social Psychology

NONVERBAL COMMUNICATION

As crucial as verbal language is to cognition, some psychologists think that in face-to-face encounters NONVERBAL COMMUNICATION expresses even more information. This group exercise will examine nonverbal communication in the following forms:

Channel of Expression. Verbal language is usually communicated through one channel at a time, that is, it is either spoken or written. Nonverbal communication encompasses the visual, kinesthetic, and auditory senses. Gender Differences. There is some debate about the differences in nonverbal communication between the genders. The overlap in men's and women's methods of sending and receiving nonverbal messages is great. However, small but important differences partially explain interpersonal communication difficulties between men and women.

Materials: None

Procedure: 1.   As a group list all the possible methods of nonverbal communication as well as the messages that each of those forms of nonverbal communication express.

2.   As a group list and discuss all possible ways in which men and women send and/or receive nonverbal messages.

3.   You are to observe two different groups of people for at least 15 minutes per group. These groups must have 3 or more people and can be in any environment where they are interacting. For example, students in the student lounge, family at a restaurant, people at a sporting event, etc. Sit far enough away from the group you are observing so that you cannot hear this conversation. Take note of all facial expressions, gestures, fast movement, leaning in or out from people body position, head movements, space between people, etc.

Record your results for both groups on your laboratory report form.

** Remember we are only focusing in on nonverbal communication. Do not try to make assumptions about what is being said. Non-verbal and verbal communication cannot be separated without diminishing the accuracy of communication as a whole.

Answer the summary questions on your laboratory report form(s).

LABORATORY REPORT FORM: NONVERBAL COMMUNICATION

Group #1

> Number of people:
> Sex of people:
> Approximate ages of each person:

Summary of what you observed:

List specific behaviors observed:

Facial Expressions:

Gestures:

Foot Movements:

Body Positions:

Head Movements:

Space Between People:

LABORATORY REPORT FORM: NONVERBAL COMMUNICATION – CONT.

Group #2

> Number of people:
> Sex of people:
> Approximate ages of each person:

Summary of what you observed:

List specific behaviors observed:

Facial Expressions:

Gestures:

Foot Movements:

Body Positions:

Head Movements:

Space Between People:

LABORATORY REPORT FORM: NONVERBAL COMMUNICATION – CONT.

Summary Questions:

1.   What differences (if any) did you notice between individuals and the groups?

2.   What type of nonverbal communication was the most expressive or had the most impact on the communication process?

3.   What type of nonverbal communication was used the most by all individuals observed?

GROUP PROCESSES

How people work together in a group to reach decisions has been widely studied by psychologists and sociologists. There is a distinct process that evolves when a group of people must resolve an issue. What is this process? Is it effective? How does it make the individual feel? You will experience this process in the following experiment.

Materials: Story in your laboratory manual.

Procedure: You will divide into groups of 5 people. You as a group must come up with a unanimous decision on the following issue.

Issue: A group of 15 people are traveling in a space craft on their way to colonize a planet. It is necessary to colonize this planet with human life.

While traveling through space, there is a malfunction in the oxygen system. There is enough oxygen remaining for 8 people to arrive safely to the planet. Seven people must be eliminated so that all 15 will not die.

You as a group are to decide which 7 are to be eliminated. Fill in this information on your Laboratory Report Form. Below are the 15 people.

	Name	Age	Description
1.	Ann Jones	6 Mos.	Infant daughter of Mrs. Jones. She is still nursing, good health.
2.	Rebecca Jones	27	Divorced, one infant child. Unable to have more children.
3.	Susan Smith	40	Reformed prostitute, divorced, likes to work with children.
4.	Dr. Abernathy	72	Medical doctor – still practicing. Experiencing some cardiovascular problems.

GROUP PROCESSES – CONT.

	Name	Age	Description
5.	John Stevens	21	Former Mr. America High School dropout. Interested in electronics.
6.	Mrs. Hammitt	32	Divorced, advanced degree in education, good teacher.
7.	Heather Hammitt	7	2nd grade, average student, Mrs. Hammitt's daughter.
8.	Rabbi Levi	51	Jewish Rabbi. Good health. Active in liberal politics – socialism.
9.	Dr. Weaver	36	Ph.D. in psychology. University Professor 1 child. Wife recently died.
10.	Harry Weaver	13	Son of Dr. Weaver. Physically healthy but retarded with I.Q. of 70.
11.	Miss Davis	28	Unmarried, nurse, black, does not date men.
12.	Mr. Porter	24	Comes from very deprived background. Married with pregnant wife. Likes to spend a lot of time alone.
13.	Mrs. Porter	22	Wife of Mr. Porter. Seven months pregnant. College graduate in music.
14.	Mr. Jennings	29	Atheist, history of emotional problems in his final year of medical school.
15.	Peter Russell	19	Freshman in college. Average, no major.

LABORATORY REPORT FORM: GROUP PROCESSES

List the 7 people your group would eliminate and why.

1._____ why?

2._____ why?

3._____ why?

4. _____ why?

5._____ why?

6._____ why?

7._____ why?

Summary Questions:

1.   Did you agree with the group? If not, why did you conform?

2.   What values were important to your group? (age, sex, career, etc.)

3.   Describe the process your group used to reach each decision.

4.   How difficult was it for your group to reach agreement?

JUROR BIAS SCALE

The two surveys you will be taking are excerpts from Kassin and Wrightman's (1993) Juror Bias Scale.

Materials: Reasonable Doubt Scale and Probability of Commission Scale

Procedure: Complete both scales. Add the scores so that there is one total score for juror bias.

Answer the summary questions on your laboratory report form(s).

REASONABLE DOUBT SCALE

Directions: For each of the following statements indicate the degree to which you personally agree with the statement. If you strongly agree with an item, respond with a number 5. Make a response of 4 if you mildly agree with the item—that is, if you think the item is generally more true than untrue. Make a response of 3 if you feel the item is about equally true and untrue. Make a response of 2 if you mildly disagree with the item—that is, if you think the item is generally more untrue than true. If you strongly disagree with the item, make a response of 1.

5 expresses strong agreement

4 expresses mild agreement

3 expresses that it's a toss-up

2 expresses mild disagreement

1 expresses strong disagreement

_____1.   A defendant should be found guilty if 11 out of 12 jurors vote guilty.

_____2.   Too often jurors, out of pure sympathy, hesitate to convict someone who is guilty.

_____3.   The death penalty is cruel and inhumane.

_____4.   For serious crimes like murder, a defendant should be found guilty as long as there is a 90% chance that he or she committed the crime.

_____5.   Extenuating circumstances should not be considered: If a person commits a crime, then that person should be punished.

_____6.   Too many innocent people are wrongly imprisoned.

_____7.   If a majority of the evidence (but not all of it) suggests that the defendant committed the crime, the jury should vote not guilty.

_____8.   If the defendant committed a victimless crime like gambling or possession of marijuana, he or she should never be convicted.

PROBABILITY OF COMMISSION SCALE

Directions: For each of the following statements indicate the degree to which you personally agree with the statement. If you strongly agree with an item, respond with a number 5. Make a response of 4 if you mildly agree with the item—that is, if you think the item is generally more true than untrue. Make a response of 3 if you feel the item is about equally true and untrue. Make a response of 2 if you mildly disagree with the item—that is, if you think the item is generally more untrue than true. If you strongly disagree with the item, make a response of 1.

5 expresses strong agreement

4 expresses mild agreement

3 expresses that it's a toss-up

2 expresses mild disagreement

1 expresses strong disagreement

_____1.   If a suspect runs from the police, then he or she probably committed the crime.

_____2.   In most cases where the accused presents a strong defense, it is only because of a good lawyer.

_____3.   Out of 100 people brought to trial, at least 75 are guilty of the crime with which they are charged.

_____4.   Defense lawyers don't really care about guilt or innocence; they are just in business to make money.

_____5.   Generally, the police make an arrest only when they are sure about who committed the crime.

_____6.   Circumstantial evidence is too weak to use in court.

_____7.   Many accident claims filed against insurance companies are phony.

_____8.   The defendant is often a victim of his or her own bad reputation.

_____9.   If the grand jury recommends that a person be brought to trail, then he or she probably committed the crime.

JUROR BIAS SCALE – CONT.

Summary Questions:

1. What was your total score from both scales?

2. Would you ever be willing to vote for the death penalty for a convicted murderer if you were on the jury? (please circle one):

   YES   NO

3. What is your gender? (please circle one):

   FEMALE   MALE

REFERENCES

Bem. W.L. (1974). The Measurement of Psychological Androgyny. Journal of Consulting and Clinical Psychology. p. 42, 155-162.

Benson, H. (1975). The Relaxation Response. Morrow: New York.

Coren, S., Porac, C., and Ward, L. (1984). Sensation and Perception. (2nd ed). Academic Press: Orlando, Fla.

Davis, Stephen F. and Palladino, Joseph J. Psychology, Prentice Hall Inc. 1995.

Ekman, P. and Friesen, W. (1975). Unmasking the Face. Prentice Hall: Englewood Cliffs, N.J.

Gardner, R.M. (1980). Exercises for General Psychology. Prentice Hall: Englewood Cliffs, N.J.

Golden, C. (1978). Stroop Color and Word Test. Odessa, FL: Psychological Assessment Resources, Inc.

Gray, W.A. and Gerrard. B.A. (1981). Understanding Yourself and Others: A Student Activity Book of Psychological Experiments and Activities. Harper & Row: New York, NY.

Hay, J.C. (1991). PSYCHWORD (2nd ed.). New York, NY: McGraw Hill.

Holland, J. and Skinner, B.F. (1961). Analysis of Behavior: A Program for Self-Instruction. New York, NY: McGraw Hill.

Holmes, T.H. and Rahe, R.H. (1967). The Social Readjustment Rating Scale. Journal of Psychosomatic Research, p. 22, 213-218.

Insel, P.M. and Roth, W.T. (1994). Core Concepts in Health, (7th ed). Mayfield: Palo Alto, CA.

Matlin, M. Perception. Copyright by Allyn and Bacon, Inc.

REFERENCES – CONT.

Myers, E.B. and Briggs, C.C. (1987). Myers-Briggs Type Indicator. Palo Alto, CA: Consulting Psychological Press, Inc.

Raven, B.H. and French, J. (1958). Raven's Progressive Matrices. Cleveland, OH: Psychological Corporation.

Schulz, R. (1978). Basic Life Expectancy. Psychology of Death, Dying, and Bereavement. McGraw-Hill: New York.

Vokey, J.R. and Read, J.D. (1985). "Sublimina Messages: Between the Devil and the Media." American Psychologist, p. 40 (11).

Zuckerman, M. (1979). Sensation Seeking: Beyond the Optimal Level of Arousal. Erlbaum: Hillsdale, N.J.